PLANTS OF THE BIBLE

Plants of the Bible

A GARDENER'S GUIDE

Daan Smit

A LION BOOK

Oxford · Batavia · Sydney

SOURCES CONSULTED:

A. Alon, *The Natural History of the Land of the Bible*, London, 1969

A.W. Andersen, *Plants of the Bible*, London, 1956

Anonymous, Fauna and Flora of the Bible, United Bible Societies, U.S.A., 1972

J.H. Balfour, *Botany and Religion*, Edinburgh, 1859

J.H. Balfour, *The Plants of the Bible: Trees and Shrubs*, London, 1857

M. Chaouat, *A New Survey of the Plant Aloe in the Bible*, Jerusalem, z.j. 1990

Dapper, *Nauwkeurige Beschrijvingen der Afrikaenschen Gewesten*, Amsterdam, 1668 (1676)

R. Dodonaeus, *Herbarius oft Cruydt-Boeck*, Antwerp, 1644

M. van Ede, *Bijbelse planten in onze tuin*, The Hague, z.j. 1935

M.H. van Es, *Planten uit de Bijbel*, Amsterdam, 1980

J. Feliks, *Plantworld of the Bible*, Israel, 1968

A. Goor and M. Nurock, *The Fruits of the Holy Land*, Jerusalem, 1968

W.H. Groser, *Scripture Natural History I, The trees and plants mentioned in the Bible*, London, 1888

N. Hareuveni, *Flowers in the Land of the Bible I*, Kiryat Ono, 1972

N. Hareuveni, *Fruit in the Land of the Bible I and II*, Kiryat Ono, 1972–1973

F.N. Hepper, *Bible Plants at Kew*, London, 1981

F.N. Hepper, *Planting a Bible Garden*, London, 1987

I. Lilias Trotter, *Parables of the Christ-life*, London, z.j. 1900

H.N. Moldenke, *Plants of the Bible*, New York, 1952

T. Monod, *Les arbres à encens (Boswellia sacra) dans le Hadramaout (Yémen du sud)*, Bull. Mus. natn. Hist. nat., Paris, 4e ser., I, 1979, section B., no. 3: 131:169

T. Monod, *Les rosas de Santa Marya de Gil Eanes (1434)*, Lisbon, 1978

G. Pabst, (ed.), *Kölner's medizinal Pflanzen (Vol. I, II, III)* 1887–1898

L.I. Rabinowits, *Torah and Flora*, Jerusalem 1977

J.J. Scheuchzer, *Geestelijke natuurkunde*, Amsterdam, 1735

D. Smit, *Planten uit de Bijbel (brochure)*, Amsterdam z.j. 1980

C.J.S. Thompson, *The Mystic Mandrake*, Plymouth, 1934

G. Thurlon, *Mythen en mysteries uit de Bijbel*, Amsterdam, 1977

A.v.d. Wal, *Planten uit de Bijbel, een systematische literatuurlijst*, Amsterdam, 1982

W. Walker, *All the Plants of the Bible*, New York, 1957

H.W. Zeller, *Wild Flowers of the Holy Land*, London, 1875

M. Zohari, *Het plantenrijk van het land van de Bijbel*, Zwolle, 1982

World copyright © 1990 D-Books International Ltd, Kidderminster, UK.

This translation copyright © 1992 Lion Publishing plc, Oxford, UK.

Text and illustrations copyright © 1990 by Daan Smit, Haarlem, Netherlands.

Copyright of Bible translations:

The Holy Bible, New International Version © 1973, 1978, 1984 International Bible Society

New Jerusalem Bible © 1985 Darton, Longman and Todd Ltd and Doubleday and Company, Inc.

Published by
Lion Publishing plc
Sandy Lane West, Oxford, England
ISBN 0 7459 2147 7

Lion Publishing Corporation
1705 Hubbard Avenue, Batavia, Illinois 60510, USA
ISBN 0 7459 2147 7

Albatross Books Pty Ltd
PO Box 320, Sutherland, NSW 2232, Australia
ISBN 0 7324 0594 7

First English edition 1992

Translation by Tony Langham and Plym Peters

Printed and bound in Czechoslovakia

CONTENTS

This is a complete listing of plants referred to in the book.

A page number in **bold** indicates the Latin name of a main entry with full description.

A page number in parentheses similarly indicates the Latin name of a plant which is illustrated.

This is a book for gardeners! In contrast with many books about Bible plants, this one not only describes the plants which are mentioned in the Old and New Testaments, but also tells you how to grow them.

The idea of putting together such a book came about during the centenary celebrations of the Free University of Amsterdam, held between 24 September and 24 October 1980. The celebrations included an exhibition on the subject of 'Plants in the Bible'. It was extremely popular, and showed just how much interest there was among the general public in actually growing the plants mentioned in the Bible.

Many of the species of plants referred to in the Bible can be grown quite easily. It is not absolutely essential to have a garden: a number of Bible plants will flourish indoors. Some of the most popular pot plants that are readily available are in fact Bible plants: these include cyclamen, pomegranate, oleander, myrtle, olive, laurel, date palm and cypress. Madonna lilies and dill are Bible plants that you can buy as cut flowers. We can no longer imagine life without some of the crops which are mentioned in the Bible, such as onions, leeks, oats, barley, millet, lentils, chicory and endive.

In the course of the centuries there has often been some confusion about which plants can really be considered to be Bible plants. For example, it is often supposed that the orange, the passion flower and some of the plants used in depictions of the crown of thorns also belong in this category. However, in many cases these plants were imported into the Holy Land centuries after the Bible was written. As trade expanded in the course of time, increasing numbers of foreign plants were imported. Even the agave, opuntia and many other exotic plants which can now be found cultivated throughout Israel, or even growing wild, are not really indigenous plants and are not included in this book, which is restricted to the hundred or so plants mentioned in the Bible.

Although the Bible text only referred to plants by their common name, it is in most cases easy to determine with a fair degree of certainty which variety is meant. In a few cases the references are rather too general: in those instances it is only possible to guess at which particular plant is intended.

The aim of this book is not only to increase the interest in the plants mentioned in the Bible, but also to encourage many people to try and grow them. I would like to thank the association for Christian Scientific Education and the women's help group of the Free University who made it possible to publish this book on the occasion of the 110th anniversary of the Free University in 1990. In addition, I am very grateful to Boris von Dobbenburgh, the publisher of D-Books International Ltd., who devoted a great deal of care to the idea of this publication and finally published it in its present form. I would also like to thank Mr. M.H. van Es (Switzerland) for his advice on theological matters, as well as Mr. S.A. Schippers and Mrs. H.N. Schippers-Tija for editing the manuscript.

Daan Smit
Amsterdam, Summer 1990

This book is aimed primarily at providing a survey of various plants mentioned in the Bible and describing them simply and clearly for the practical gardener. Some plants have not been included, either because they are hard to grow or because it is difficult to identify them with any degree of certainty from the Bible reference.

About a hundred different Bible plants are included, arranged in alphabetical order according to their scientific names. Each entry lists the scientific name, the family name, the natural habitat and the English, Bible, Greek and Hebrew names. There is a general description of each plant, and instructions on how to grow it.

Separate chapters give general guidelines for growing plants indoors as well as outdoors, growing from seed, container gardening, propagation, and combating plant diseases.

Most of the black and white illustrations contained in the book are reproductions of woodcuts in the *Book of Herbs* by R. Dodonaeus, published in 1664. The colour plates were taken from the author's archives.

In view of the limited scope of this book, it is not possible to describe all the plants mentioned in the Bible in detail. Some of the plants which are not included are listed below under their scientific name followed by their common name (where it is known) in brackets, and by the Bible reference. This makes it possible for the interested reader to look up the quotation for a particular plant.

Lolium temulentum (weeds) Matthew 13:25
Mentha longifolia (mint) Matthew 23:23
Nigella sativa (dill) Isaiah 28:25
Origanum syriacum (oregano, hyssop) Exodus 12:22
Pinus halepensis (fir tree) Isaiah 41:19
Prunus armeniaca (apricot/apple tree) Joel 1:12
Ricinus communis (vine/gourd) Jonah 4:6
Scirpus lacustris (bullrush) Exodus 2:3
Tamarix gallica (tamarisk) Genesis 21:33
Triticum aestivum (wheat) Exodus 34:22
Triticum dicoccum (spelt) Exodus 9:32
Typha latifolia (bullrush) Exodus 2:3

NERIUM OLEANDER

1 ❧ INDOOR AND OUTDOOR GARDENING

Some of the plants mentioned in the Bible can be grown as indoor pot plants or outdoors in the garden. The species listed below are generally available.

EASY-TO-GROW HOUSEPLANTS:

Aloe barbadensis (aloe)
Cupressus sempervirens (cypress)
Cyclamen persicum hybride (cyclamen)
Cyperus papyrus (papyrus reed)
Laurus nobilis (laurel)
Myrtus communis (myrtle)
Narcissus tazetta (tazetta narcissus)
Nerium oleander (oleander)
Olea europaea (olive)
Phoenix dactylifera (date palm)
Pinus pinea (parasol pine)

EASY-TO-GROW GARDEN PLANTS:
(* means frost tender)

Acorus calamus (sweet flag)
Arundo donax (reed) *
Cercis siliquastrum (Judas tree)
Elaeagnus angustifolia (oleaster)
Hedera helix (ivy)
Morus alba (white mulberry)
Morus nigra (black mulberry)
Paliurus spina-christi (Christ's thorn) *
Platanus orientalis (oriental flame tree)
Prunus dulcis (almond)
Vitis vinifera (grape)

The plants listed as houseplants can easily be cultivated indoors, provided they are grown in a light or sunny spot which is not too warm. However, the olive and papyrus reed do tolerate heat well. As they all need to be grown in a fairly sunny spot, the plants will tend to lose a lot of moisture through evaporation, so make sure that the earth in the pot is watered regularly to keep it moist. Water the earth in the pot directly and after an hour remove the excess water from the saucer underneath or from the ornamental outer pot. Papyrus is an exception to this rule: this plant from the riverbank must have its roots constantly submerged in water.

Apart from *Phoenix dactylifera*, the plants listed in this section can be moved outside once all risk of frost has passed and the daytime temperature is fairly warm. This promotes the growth and flowering of these plants, but it is not essential, and you don't really have to worry if you don't have a garden or balcony. For further information about how to look after these plants, refer to the section on overwintering.

Growing plants listed as garden plants is much simpler. When you have bought one of these plants, plant it in the most suitable spot. It is advisable to enrich the earth before planting with some good soil and/or manure. Easy-to-work dried manure is available from good suppliers.

The varieties marked * should be covered with leaf mould, leaves or straw before the winter. When you do this it is enough merely to cover up the base of the plant.

2 ❧ RAISING PLANTS FROM SEED

The various plants mentioned in the Bible can be classified into three groups:

A Non-hardy trees and shrubs

B Hardy trees and shrubs

C Annuals (**A**), biennials (**B**) and herbaceous perennials (**P**)

THE PLANTS IN GROUP A INCLUDE:

Acacia tortilis (acacia)
Capparis spinosa (capers)
Ceratonia siliqua (carob)
Cinnamomum zeylanicum (cinnamon)
Cistus incanus ssp. *creticus* (Cistus)
Commiphora myrrha (myrrh)
Cupressus sempervirens (cypress)
Ficus sycomorus (sycamore fig)
Gossypium herbaceum (cotton)
Juniperus oxycedrus (juniper)
Laurus nobilis (laurel)
Liquidambar orientalis (oriental amber tree)
Lygos raetam (broom)
Myrtus communis (myrtle)
Nerium oleander (oleander)
Olea europaea (olive)
Phoenix dactylifera (date palm)
Pistacia vera (pistachio)
Punica granatum (pomegranate)
Quercus aegilops (oak)
Quercus ilex (holm oak)
Quercus suber (cork oak)
Rosa phoenicea (rose)
Sarcopoterium spinosum (sarcopoterium)
Styrax officinalis (storax)

THE PLANTS IN GROUP B INCLUDE:

Atriplex halimus (tree purslane)
Cedrus libani (cedar)
Cercis siliquastrum (Judas tree)
Eleagnus angustifolia (oleaster)
Ficus carica (fig)
Juglans regia (walnut)
Lycium barbatum (thorn bush)
Morus nigra (black mulberry)

Morus alba (white mulberry)
Pinus pinea (parasol pine)
Platanus orientalis (oriental plane)
Prunus dulcis (almond)
Vitis vinifera (grape)

THE PLANTS IN GROUP C INCLUDE:

Acanthus syriacus (acanthus) **P**
Aegilops uniaristata (Aegilops) **A**
Agrostemma githago (corn cockle) **P**
Allium cepa (onion) **A**
Allium porrum (leek) **A**
Allium X proliferum (Egyptian onion) **P**
Allium sativum (garlic) **P**
Anastatica hierochuntica (Rose of Jericho) **A**
Anemone coronaria (anemone) **P**
Anethum graveolens (dill) **A**
Astragallus gummifer (milk vetch) **P**
Avena sterilis (oats) **A**
Butomus umbellatus (flowering rush) **P**
Brassica nigra (black mustard) **A**
Carthamus glaucus (thistle) **A**
Carthamus tinctorius (safflower) **A**
Centaurea calcitrapa (star thistle) **A**
Chrysanthemum coronarium (crown daisy) **A**
Cichorium intybus (chicory) **B**
Citrullus colocynthis (bitter-apple) **A**
Citrullus lanatus (watermelon) **A**
Cnicus benedictus (blessed thistle) **A**
Coriandrum sativum (coriander) **A**
Crocus sativus (saffron) **P**
Cucumis sativus (cucumber) **A**
Cuminum cyminum (cumin) **A**
Dictamnus albus (burning bush) **P**
Ecballium elaterium (squirting cucumber) **A**
Eruca vesicaria ssp. *sativa* (rocket, hedge mustard) **A**
Ferula galbaniflua (giant fennel) **P**
Hordeum vulgare (barley) **A**
Hyacinthus orientalis (hyacinth) **P**
Isatis tinctoria (woad) **B**
Iris pseudacorus (yellow flag) **P**
Lactuca sativa (lettuce) **A**
Lens culinaris (lentil) **A**
Lilium candidum (Madonna lily) **P**
Linum usitatissimum (flax) **A**
Mandragora autumnalis (mandrake) **P**
Mandragora officinarum (mandrake) **P**
Nasturtium officinale (watercress) **P**

Notobasis syriaca (thistle) **B**
Nymphaea lotus (waterlily) **P**
Ornithogalum narbonense (Star of Bethlehem) **P**
Panicum miliaceum (millet) **A**
Papaver rhoeas (poppy) **A**
Rubia tinctorium (madder) **P**
Rumex acetosa (sheep's sorrel) **P**
Ruscus aculeatus (butcher's broom) **P**
Ruta graveolens (rue) **P**
Scolymus maculatus (golden thistle) **A**
Silybum marianum (Our Lady's thistle) **B**
Taraxacum officinale (dandelion) **P**
Tulipa montana (tulip) **P**
Urtica pilulifera (stinging-nettle) **A**
Vicia faba (broad bean)

Sow the seeds of plants in group A in early spring. It is best to sow them in a small flowerpot filled with moist peat. Cover the seeds with another layer of moist peat about as thick as the seeds themselves. Then water the seeds generously and place the whole pot in a plastic bag and tie it up at the top.

The seeds will germinate in a warm spot on the windowsill. Each type of plant has its own germination time. When the young plants have grown one or two true leaves you can repot them, either separately in small plant pots or with several young plants together in a large pot. A good potting mix could be made from four parts of peat to one part of well-rotted manure. Potting compost available from specialist shops will also usually do well. As the plants grow bigger, they can be repotted into a larger size of pot.

All the plants listed under this section have to be grown indoors in a light spot, preferably sunny, and not too warm. When all all risk of frost has passed, you can dig the plant, still in its pot, into a sunny spot in the garden. Halfway through the summer you can take the plants and pots out of the soil and repot them. Then you can put them back and feed two or three times with artificial fertilizer. In about the middle of October, or before frost threatens, bring the plants back indoors and leave them throughout the winter in a cool, preferably sunny spot.

The seeds which fall under group B come from woody plants which will withstand a few degrees of frost. Sow as described above, but then dig the seeds into the garden with the pot. In some cases it will take a year for the seeds to germinate, and sometimes you will wait for results in vain because the seeds have been eaten by birds or insects. To prevent this, it's a good idea to cover the seeds with some fine netting. Once the young plants have appeared they can be potted on. Some will make sufficient growth to be planted out within a year; others will take several years to reach a suitable size.

The seeds listed under group C include annuals, biennials and perennials. The different varieties are marked in the following way:

ANNUAL **A**

BIENNIAL **B**

PERENNIAL **P**

The best time to sow all these varieties is in late spring. You can sow them directly outside where you want them to grow. Annuals and biennials should not be sown too close together, as it is usually difficult or impossible to replant them later on. Sow perennials in rows and when they are big enough (approximately 5cm tall), plant out the young plants individually or in groups of three to five together. As they are sun-loving plants, choose a light and sunny position for them. During the growing season the tall varieties in particular must be staked, or they will flop over.

At the end of the season it is a good idea to collect the seed of the varieties which you wish to grow again next season. This applies particularly to the annuals. Leave the seeds to dry, pick out any debris, and then store them in a cool, dry place until it is sowing time again.

3 ❧ PLANT NAMES

In 1752 Carl Linnaeus (1707–1778) introduced the system of double names—the binomial system—for plants. Previously, plant names had been very long-winded, because the actual names contained a short description. Nowadays the name of a plant consists of two words in Latin. The first word indicates the genus, and the second the particular species concerned. The genus name is spelled with a capital letter, and both words are italicized.

The naming of plants is often a complicated business. In many cases the names are changed in a way that does not, at first, seem very logical. For example, why is the mother-of-thousands, which was previously known as *Saxifraga sarmentosa*, now known as *Saxifraga stolonifera?* The reason is that when it was given its scientific name, its earlier name and description were unknown. When botantists discover that a particular plant has been described in older books under a completely different scientific (Linnean) name, the older name applies.

Botanists who find an as yet unnamed plant growing in the wild have to examine it carefully to determine what group of plants it belongs to. It will then be given the correct genus name, and a suitable species name that describes it accurately. This is then published by the author concerned, in a scientific journal or thesis. The name is fixed from the time that it is published.

In scientific articles the name of a plant also contains the name of the author who first described the plant. This Latin name and description makes sense to botanists in every country, and the author's name makes it much easier to find the first description of a newly-discovered plant.

FURTHER SUBDIVISIONS
A species may be subdivided further. The abbreviation 'subsp.' (subspecies) indicates a natural variant with its own natural habitat, for example *Euphorbia characias* subsp. *characias*. The variety ('var.') has a slightly different botanical form.

FORMS AND CULTIVARS
Very often many forms (f.) or cultivars (cvs.) of one particular species can be found. These may have developed spontaneously, for example, when a yellow bloom appears on a red flowering rose. This sort of deviation is called a sport.

However, most cultivars are obtained by a process of cross-fertilization and selection. The description of a new cultivated variety may be published in every modern language and fancy names are used to describe the plant. These can be translated into any language, such as, for example, 'Fireball', 'Boule de feu', 'Feuerball' and 'Vuurbal'. These fancy names should always be spelled with a capital letter and in quotation marks.

INTERGENERIC HYBRIDS
A plant which results from the cross-fertilization of two genera is identified with an 'X' and a name that is based on the two parent genera. For example, the cross-fertilization of *Fatsia japonica* and *Hedera helix* is called *X Fatshedera*.

HYBRIDS WITHIN A GENUS
A cross-fertilization of two species within a genus used to be given a Latin name. This is no longer the case and cross-fertilizations are given fancy names instead. Existing Latin names have become so established for many hybrids, however, that they have not been changed. Instead an 'X' sign is placed in front of the name of the species, such as *Colutea X media* (from *Colutea arborescens X Colutea orientalis*), or *Forsythia X intermedia* (from *Forsythia suspensa X Forsythia viridissima*).

GRAFTED HYBRIDS
These occur when one plant is grafted to another and the cells join in such a way as to produce a new plant. These are indicated with a plus sign, for example, + *Labernocytisus*, a graft hybrid between *Laburnum* and *Cytisus* and + *Crataegomespilus*, from + *Crataegus* and *Mespilus*.

Many of the Bible plants which are not hardy and are grown in pots or tubs will flourish better if they are put out in the garden during the summer months. However, to protect them from the frost they should not be put out before late spring. Here are some general tips which can help the plants to thrive while potted.

TYPES OF SOIL AND FERTILIZERS

In many cases the natural habitat of a plant will give an indication of the type of soil in which it grows. For example, plants from the tropical rainforest will generally do better in a soil rich in humus (organic matter) than in a bare, dry place. In order to find out what types of soil and fertilizers, or combinations of these, will suit a particular plant best, a brief summary of the most important and commonly used types is given below.

In general terms the different types of soil easily available to us can be divided into soil that is rich in humus and soil that is poor in humus. Soils rich in humus include deciduous woodland, coniferous woodland, and areas where the soil is rich in peat. There is virtually no humus in clay and sandy soils. In general, pot plants thrive best in soil with a high percentage of humus. This contains ample nutrients which are needed for growth. These nutrients are present in large quantities in the soil of deciduous as well as coniferous woodland, particularly when the mixture has almost entirely rotted down. In some cases the level of acidity (pH) is too high or too low. In order to determine the level precisely a sample of soil is taken and its acidity tested in a laboratory. Usually the quantity of soil used for pot plants is so small that it is not even worthwhile to do this. In that case the acidity is determined more or less by rule of thumb. Soils rich in humus are fairly acidic (they have a low pH) and this is particularly true of peat. Most plants like a pH value of 5.5–6.5. The potting compost that can be bought in bags is based on this value. However, a small percentage of garden plants require an even more acidic soil than the usual mixture. In this case, it is best to use pure leaf mould, soil from coniferous woodland, peat, or a mixture of these. In contrast, a small group of plants does better in a less acidic soil, and therefore prefers a different basic mixture. A less acidic mixture can be prepared by mixing potting compost with soil rich in humus, adding lime for a particularly alkaline soil. Garden sand, particularly sharp sand or river sand, is sometimes added to the basic mixtures to improve the drainage. It has no significance in terms of nutrients. People used to put fragments of broken pot at the bottom of flower pots, to improve the drainage. Today you can buy fired clay pellets in various sizes instead.

A soil may be rich in humus, but this does not mean that it also contains much fertilizer. As a rule, this has to be added as well. Either organic or inorganic matter can be used for this. If organic manure is used, it is best to use well-rotted material, such as cow dung or stable manure which has been rotting down for a year and has therefore largely broken down to a crumbly soil-like consistency. It is also possible to use dried organic manure, but do remember that this is considerably more concentrated. Either can be obtained from garden centres.

Alternatively, there are different types of inorganic fertilizers, the artificial fertilizers. If you use these, it is a good idea to get plenty of information. Plant nutrients which are added to the water in the watering can as extra fertilizer are inorganic preparations of various different compositions and concentrations. Before using them it is important to check up how they should be used.

There are also organic fertilizers made from animal products such as bone meal, blood and horn. These are available either in a pure form or in a mixture. The advantage of a mixture is that fertilizers with a blood base act very rapidly, while the nutrients from bone meal and horn-based meal are released more slowly. The disadvantage of the last two fertilizers is that they have an extremely unpleasant smell, and are therefore only suitable for use in the open air. These fertilizers are very suitable for plants in outdoor tubs as there is very little risk of overfeeding.

REPOTTING

Before putting some plants out in the open air it is as well to make sure that they are in the right size of pot. As the plant grows it will need a larger size than it did. A rich soil for repotting can be prepared by combining, for example, one part of peat with one part potting compost and one part of well-rotted manure. If these are not available, you can also use commercial composting mixtures.

The term 'pot plant' is really a bit misleading. No plants naturally grow in containers. However, container gardening is easy and convenient, and certainly some plants do very well when grown in this way. They certainly brighten up our homes and workplaces, as well as outdoor areas.

Container growing has a long history. For centuries the Japanese have practised the art of bonsai—growing trees in tiny pots or trays. In this case, the aim is actually to keep the plants small. A bonsai survives on the edge of existence, but with careful treatment some shrubs and trees can live like this for decades. The example of the bonsai reveals how a plant is often very adaptable, and shows that it is not always necessary to use fresh soil and compost.

Terracotta pots have been used for many years. They come in all sorts of sizes, from those no bigger than a nutshell to outdoor planters suitable for small trees. The price varies accordingly! For orchids there are special pots with a large number of openings in the sides and in the bottom. (The pots imported from China are very beautiful.) There are also special tall, thin pots for lilies and palms. Azaleas are often grown in broad, shallow pots. These shapes are related to the natural shape of the root system: in lilies some roots may even develop at the top of the bowl, while palms often have a tap root.

Recently plastic pots have become increasingly popular. They are much cheaper, lightweight, easy to stack and keep clean because of the smooth sides. They are very popular in nurseries and plants grow well in them. But watch out that you don't overwater plants in plastic pots, which conserve moisture much better than the traditional terracotta pot.

A clay pot is porous, which means that a great deal of moisture evaporates through the sides of the pot. As air also penetrates through the side of the pot, many of the roots grow along the sides, *outside* the ball of earth, so that it soon seems as though the pot is too small. As a large number of nutrient salts can accumulate at the edges, as a result of evaporation through the sides of the pot, the roots may start to die off. On top of the other advantages of plastic pots, this is a good reason for many nurseries no longer to use earthenware pots. However, if earthenware pots are used, it is not so important to be fussy about watering the plants. Excess water will evaporate, and the colour of the pot more or less indicates the need for water (light red means that the earth is dry; dark red that it is wet). As long as you know this, little can go wrong with watering.

When a plant is put in a pot for the first time after sowing or taking cuttings, this is called potting the plant. If a plant outgrows its pot, it is given a larger one with fresh soil. This is called repotting or potting on.

If a plant deteriorates, the first thing to check is whether it might need repotting. Pick up the plant and see whether there are many roots coming out of the hole at the bottom. If this is the case, the chances are that the plant needs repotting, so that the new root tips, which have to absorb the water and nutrients needed by the plant, are in the soil.

If a plant has been given too much water, the roots will die off. They have a brown colour and when they are cut, they are also brown, in contrast with the light or light brown colour of healthy roots. The soil may have an unpleasant smell. In this case, repotting is also a good idea.

It is also possible for the pot to become very dirty. Chalky deposits can lead to white marks, and algae formation can cause green marks. In this case, take a new pot and throw away the dirty one immediately. Even the broken bits can no longer be used.

When you are repotting, use a pot which is only slightly larger than the last one. In a large pot the roots will grow rapidly, but this certainly does not necessarily mean that the plant will also flourish above the ground. It can also flourish too much: an oleander may grow more leaves than flowers, and that is certainly not what you want!

Pots must be clean. Used pots should be scrubbed thoroughly, if possible with soda, and then rinsed. Plastic pots are easier to clean than earthenware ones. Nevertheless, mould spores, which can be very small, and insect eggs should all be removed. New earthenware pots should be placed in water for some time before they are used, so that they can absorb plenty of water. Make sure that there are always different sizes available, and clean them before putting them away.

To repot plants you will need pots of the right size, fresh potting compost (a homemade composition or a brand approved by a testing laboratory), a good place to work where you can make a bit of a mess, bits of broken pot or some expanded clay pellets for the bottom (for drainage) and a watering can. Before removing the plant from its pot, it should be submerged under water in its pot, or be thoroughly watered. The wet root clump will remain whole, and this is important for plants, which hate root disturbance. Before placing it in a new pot, remove the top few centimetres of earth, which often have a high concentration of minerals which can damage the roots.

Then add the new soil and press it down.

Strong plants (such as the aloe) can be repotted in a drier state: in this case the old soil is easier to shake off. Smash the pot or cut it if there are many roots poking through the bottom or attached to the side of the pot. You will soon notice whether this is necessary when you hold the plant upside down and then tap the pot smartly against the edge of the table. Support the plant with the fingers of your other hand, just above the edge of the pot. Large plants will have to be removed from the old pot in more or less the same way by two people: either break the pot or loosen the plant round the edge. When you have finished doing this, place broken bits of pot or clay pellets in the bottom of the new pot. This prevents the hole in the bottom of the pot from becoming blocked with compacted earth.

If the clump of earth is not too large, place a thin layer of soil at the bottom of the new pot and then put the plant into it. There should be some space remaining around the sides. Fill this with fresh soil and then press it down with your fingers or thumbs. Loose soil dries out very quickly. The top should now be at the same level or slightly below that in the old pot. If the pot has been filled up with soil, make sure that it is not too full. Some space should be left to water the plant, or the pot will flood every time it is watered, which means you may not give the plant enough water.

Watering is the next thing to do. It is always a good idea to spray the plant, because this means that less water will evaporate and the plant will not wilt so readily. The roots are always slightly damaged by repotting, which means that less water is absorbed, though evaporation through the leaves simply continues. The warmer the weather, the more water evaporates through the leaves, so as well as spraying, keep the plant out of the sun. You can even cover it with polythene. Water moderately, but spray generously.

Plants grow most during the early spring, and therefore this is the most suitable time for repotting most plants. Plants with flowers or buds are repotted after they have flowered, so that you do not interfere with the flowering. Only repot a plant when it is really necessary, and never more than once a year.

HARDEN OFF GRADUALLY
If plants cultivated in a pot or in a tub were simply put outdoors they could be easily damaged. First they slowly have to get used to the new conditions; this is called 'hardening off'. Large fluctuations in temperature can be prevented by waiting to put out the plants until late spring. If it is still too cold at that time, just wait until the outside temperature increases slightly. If the temperature changes too abruptly, the leaves can easily be burnt by the sun, so it is best to put

out plants in rainy or cloudy weather when the temperature is mild. Ideally this kind of weather should continue for a few days. If, however, the weather is sunny, the plants should be protected against the direct rays of the sun by screening them with a piece of old, preferably coarse-meshed, net curtain. Leaf burn is particularly bad for plants which only form a few new leaves every year. For rapidly growing plants it is not so serious: if the burnt stems and leaves are cut back, the plant will soon grow again. After about two weeks the protective net curtain can be removed and the plants will have been hardened off.

WATERING AND FEEDING
Once the plants have acclimatized they will soon start to grow. To encourage growth it is a good idea to feed them. This should only be done when the earth round the roots is really moist; if necessary, the plant should be well watered first. If a solution of artificial fertilizer is poured onto dry earth, this can cause burning, leading to brown edges on the leaves, or even completely dried up leaves.

The amount of fertilizer needed differs from plant to plant, and it is very important to use the correct quantity. In general, rapidly growing plants need additional feeding every week throughout the summer. For slow-growing plants, this should be restricted to once every two to four weeks. On the other hand, cacti and succulents should only be given a little, at most twice a season. If they are fed too much, the plant outgrows its strength and loses its characteristic shape.

MAINTENANCE
Plants left outdoors will grow rapidly if the weather is good. The earth in the pot soon becomes overgrown with roots, and new roots start to seek food outside the pot. This overcrowding of the roots can be a great nuisance when it is time to bring the plants back indoors. Therefore it is advisable to turn the pots through 180° every four to six weeks, pushing away the excess roots with your thumb. Afterwards water the plant well to prevent the leaves from wilting. Sometimes you will have to repot a plant with excessive root growth.

If you plan to dig your containers into the garden soil in the summer, it's a good idea to use terracotta pots, so that they can absorb water through the porous sides even in dry weather. On the other hand, if the plants are placed on a balcony or veranda, a plastic pot is better, as this retains moisture longer.

SITING PLANTS
As remarked earlier, not all Bible plants can be grown outside in summer. The amount of light or shade also plays an extremely important role in the development

of the plant. Here is a brief guide to finding the best position for all the plants described in this book.

Plants which should be grown indoors all year round in a light spot by an east or west facing window:
Cupressus, Cyclamen, Cyperus, Laurus, Myrtus, Nerium, Olea, Phoenix, Pinus, Aloe.

Annual plants which can be grown either in full sunlight or in a semi-shaded spot in the summer months:
Aegilops, Agrostemma, Anastatica, Anethum, Avena, Brassica, Carthamus, Centaurea, Chrysanthemum, Cichorium, Citrullus, Cnicus, Coriandrum, Cucumis, Ecballium, Eruca, Hordeum, Lactuca, Lens, Linum, Nigella, Panicum, Papaver, Ricinus, Scolymus, Trigonella, Urtica, Vicia.

Plants which thrive in a semi-shaded spot in the garden throughout the year:
Acanthus, Anemone, Hyacinthus.

Plants which can be grown in summer in the garden either in full sunlight or in a semi-shaded spot:
Cupressus, Cyclamen, Laurus, Pinus.

Plants which can be grown in the garden throughout the year either in water or in a very damp spot in full sunlight:
Acorus, Butomus, Iris.

Plants which can be grown indoors in winter or left out in the garden all the year round:
Arundo, Paliurus, Pinus pinea.

Plants which are either fairly or completely hardy:
Acorus, Allium X proliferum, Butomus, Cedrus, Cercis,

Cichorium, Crocus, Dictamnus, Eleagnus, Hedera, Hyacinthus, Iris, Isatis, Juglans, Lilium, Morus, Nasturtium, Nymphaea, Ornithogalum, Platanus, Prunus, Rubia, Rumex, Ruscus, Ruta, Sibylum, Taraxacum, Tulipa, Vitis.

Plants which are fairly hardy, provided they are covered in winter:
Acanthus, Anemone, Arundo, Astragalus, Paliurus.

Annual plants which die off when they have flowered (so-called disposable plants):
Narcissus (paperwhite narcissus)

Plants which are put outside in full sunlight in summer:
Acacia, Acanthus, Aloe, Arundo, Cedrus, Ceratonia, Cinnamomum, Cistus, Cupressus, Ficus, Juniperus. Laurus, Liquidambar, Lygos, Myrtus, Nerium, Olea, Paliurus, Phoenix, Pinus, Pistacia, Punica, Quercus, Rosa, Sarcopoterium, Styrax, Ricinus.

Plants for the vegetable garden:
Allium, Cichorium, Cucumis, Eruca, Lactuca, Lens, Nasturtium, Rumex, Taraxacum, Vicia.

Plants for the herb garden:
Allium, Anethum, Coriandrum, Crocus, Cuminum, Laurus, Nigella, Ruta, Trigonella.

Field crops:
Avena, Hordeum, Panicum.

Plants for the fruit garden:
Citrullus, Ficus, Juglans, Morus, Olea, Phoenix, Pinus, Pistacia, Prunus, Punica.

5 ✤ CONSERVATORY AND CONTAINER PLANTS

In the eighteenth century large numbers of new plants were brought to Europe from the many journeys which were undertaken, particularly for the East India Company. It was, above all, the rich merchants who were keen to collect and cultivate as many unusual plants as possible. As there were no greenhouses at that time, they looked for ways of keeping these exotic plants indoors in the winter. The best solution that developed was the 'orangery', a glass-roofed room in which the temperature was maintained at approximately 5° C during the winter. These rooms owe their name to the orange trees which were usually grown in large tubs and brought in for the winter. Unfortunately only a few eighteenth and nineteenth century orangeries have survived, although some of the great houses of Europe have one, and conservatories are a feature of many later houses.

The many container plants that are grown all over the world today include a large number from the warmer climatic regions, from the Mediterranean to the tropics.

Laurel, orange trees, acacias, eucalyptus trees and several varieties of palm trees are included among traditional orangery plants. For Bible plants which can be grown in the same way, refer to the section on siting plants.

EASY TO KEEP THROUGH THE WINTER

All these plants need a winter temperature of approximately 5° C. The intensity of light does not play a very important role because they have a dormant period during the winter and do not grow. Plants grown in tubs have become increasingly popular, for everyone can find a spot indoors where they can be kept cool and protected from the frost. An attic or an unheated bedroom will do very well, and if necessary, a shed will suffice. From the time that the plants are brought indoors in mid-autumn to the time that they can be taken out again, they need very little moisture.

The plants should not be taken outside until the late spring, when there is no more chance of night frost.

REPOTTING CONTAINER PLANTS

The best time to repot container plants is in the middle of spring, just before they start to grow again. Often it will be necessary to prune the plants back hard, at least if this has not been done in the autumn. The advantage of pruning plants back is that roots which are damaged when the plant is placed in a new tub can recover, which strongly encourages the regrowth that is desired. If you use wooden tubs, you will probably find that the roots become attached to the inside of the tub so firmly that they are inevitably damaged when they are pulled away. Be sure to trim such plants to encourage new growth.

To avoid buying larger and more expensive tubs every time the plants are repotted, it is advisable to remove the old soil as far as possible. It is particularly important to remove the top layer of soil, for many minerals will accumulate there and after a while these are damaging to the roots.

Once the plant has been pruned and the soil has been cleaned, the plant can be placed in the newly prepared container. First check that the drainage holes are not blocked with soil or remains of old roots. Put a layer of broken pots on these holes to ensure good drainage. If the tub is not properly drained, it will fill up with water, the roots will die off and soon the whole plant will die. Put soil in on top of the shards and then repot the plant in it.

The composition of the soil for these plants, which generally prefer an acid soil, is as follows: one third peat, one third potting compost, and one third old, well-rotted manure.

FURTHER CARE

When the plant has been placed in the new tub, keep the soil fairly moist and spray regularly to encourage regrowth as much as possible. Move plants outside in late spring and place them in a warm shady spot in the garden or on the verandah. As for all plants which are placed outside after a long time indoors, it is important to ensure that they do not suffer leaf burn. You can protect them by covering them, for example, with net curtain. For optimum growth and flowering, feed a plant with artificial fertilizer every two to three weeks, as well as watering it.

Another important thing to remember is to secure the tub. Tall plants in particular can easily be blown over and damaged in a strong wind. This can be prevented by securing the containers, for example, with pieces of curved reinforced steel bars which are driven quite a long way into the ground.

AUTUMN TASKS

Although it often seems a pity to bring plants in tubs back indoors in the middle of autumn, it is absolutely essential to stick to this time. A slight night frost can be fatal. In some cases it may be necessary to prune them back hard because there is not enough room to keep them so large in the winter. If the plants were dug into the garden with their pots, they will usually have to be repotted. Try to damage the roots growing outside the pot as little as possible.

To make sure that the plants successfully survive the winter in their tubs it is important to ensure they are kept in a cool, light, well ventilated place, with a minimum temperature of 5° C. Let the soil stay fairly dry and do not add any fertilizer.

UPKEEP OF WOODEN TUBS
As wooden tubs are expensive it is important to look after them carefully. The insides are particularly vulnerable. From time to time the tubs should be emptied and dried out and treated with a recommended preparation. The outside can be treated at any time, even when there is a plant in the tub. It is not advisable to varnish the outside. After a while varnish starts to flake off, and this looks ugly; oxalic oil is better because it is absorbed by the wood and means that the tub will last longer. Nowadays, asbestos, cement, plastic and earthenware containers are also available. They are often cheaper and more durable, but not as decorative as the more traditional teak tubs.

LILIES OF THE FIELD (PAPAVER RHOEAS AND CHRYSANTHEMUM CORONARIUM)

6 &ca&o PROPAGATION: TIPS AND TECHNIQUES

PRUNING

Some plants grow so fast that they have to be pruned to be kept in hand. Fast-growing varieties can be pruned in spring, summer or autumn. Plants which have been outside for the summer and must be brought indoors before the first night frost if they are to survive, should be pruned back hard when they have been dug up. In most cases they will have produced many roots outside the pot, and if they were not pruned they would lose a great many leaves in any case. Sometimes you will have to put them in larger pots rather than damage the roots, but even then it is essential to prune them back hard. The shoots that are cut off can be used as cuttings.

TAKING CUTTINGS

There are a number of types of cuttings. With regard to the plants mentioned in the Bible, the most successful are tip and stem cuttings.

Tip cuttings are the most common. Cut the tops off the shoots that have been pruned. The length depends on the variety. A laurel top cutting may be 10–15cm long, while an oleander cutting can be as long as 30cm. For a top cutting remove the lower leaves. If necessary, simply cut away half the remaining leaves. This reduces the leaf surface, and thus lessens evaporation. In the case of plants which are sensitive to viral infections, take the precaution of disinfecting the knife in alcohol or in a flame before taking each cutting. To encourage root formation, especially with woody cuttings, use growth hormones in the form of rooting powder. As a rule, only the lower part of the cutting is dipped in this powder. When the cuttings are ready, put them in a pot with moist peat, water the cutting well, and then cover the pot with polythene to reduce evaporation. The right atmosphere for rapid root development will then form in this mini-greenhouse. Do not remove the polythene until the cutting starts to grow. Then the cuttings can be potted in the correct soil composition for each particular variety.

Stem cuttings are pieces of stem which still have leaves on them. Use an extremely sharp knife to cut them from a pruned branch, 0.5–1cm below the base of the leaf. Each piece is dipped into the rooting powder. If the leaf is large, roll it up lengthways and secure with an elastic band in order to prevent evaporation; another possibility is to cut away half the leaf. The cuttings can then be treated in the same way as tip cuttings. In general it takes longer and is more difficult for these cuttings to form roots. Often the leaf turns black after a while, which shows that the cutting has rotted. However, if it is successful, a shoot will develop from the eye just above the leaf. It is then time to remove the plastic and pot the cutting in peat.

SPLITTING/DIVIDING

Plants which do not form runners above the ground but spread by means of root stocks underground can only be propagated by dividing or splitting. Bible plants which can be divided in this way include *Acanthus, Aloe, Arundo, Cyperus, Dictamnus, Ferula, Iris, Isatis, Lilium, Nymphaea, Ornithogalum* and *Ruscus*. The best time to divide these plants is in the spring while they are being repotted or replanted. When the plant has been tapped or removed from its pot and the soil has been shaken off, use a sharp knife to cut the clump in two pieces, or more if it is large. Then the split pieces must be repotted or planted out immediately to prevent the roots from drying out. It is important to water them well. Plants with wilted leaves should be wrapped or covered in polythene for some time to stimulate root growth.

WAYS TO STIMULATE ROOT GROWTH

For woody cuttings it is often particularly important to use a preparation to promote root growth. A number of different brands are available from gardening shops.

ROOTING MEDIUM

The root formation of cuttings is fastest in moist peat. This type of soil heats up quickly because of its airy composition and remains moist for a long time. You can stimulate a more rapid root formation and prevent drying out by covering the cuttings with a plastic bag.

Cuttings of ivy or oleander also form roots very easily in water. Often they can stay in the water for a long time, particularly if some artificial fertilizer is added to the water every other week. Now and again change the water completely, to prevent an excessively high concentration of minerals.

7 ❧ PLANT DISEASES

Bible plants are vulnerable to attacks by insects and fungi, some of which are often very difficult to combat. In many cases you can look in vain for the cause of a particular disease. Draughts and dry air may affect plants cultivated indoors, and sometimes harmful insects or the germs of disease are already present in the plant when it is bought. If you are familiar with the symptoms of the various diseases, you can check for insects or mould when you buy a plant.

In most cases a beautiful, regular, green and shiny plant will be healthy. Any brown or other marks of discoloration on the leaf which should not be there mean that you should watch out. It is often more difficult to determine whether plants with variegated leaves have been infected. The most common parasites and the symptoms of infection are described below.

PARASITIC INFESTATIONS

These include insects and fungi which live on the sap or green parts of a plant. This group can be divided into insects and fungi which absorb sap and those which devour the plant.

SUCKING INSECTS

These insects survive by feeding on the plant's sap. They include scale insects, root aphis, woolly aphis, greenfly, whitefly, eelworms, root eelworms, red spider mite, and thrips.

APHIDS

The most common scourges of the plants in this book are aphids—both greenfly and blackfly. An infestation of greenfly is caused in most cases by draughts. Greenfly are light green in colour, and just a few millimetres long. They have eight legs and sometimes wings. Blackfly are comparatively rare (except in the case of broad beans, as is well known!). In general they are fairly easy to fight successfully with a nicotine-based spray.

SCALE INSECTS

These insects are sometimes more difficult to deal with, particularly when they settle between the leaf rosettes of bushy plants, such as the date palm. Soft scale insects are several millimetres long, dark brown in colour, and round in shape, while hard-coated scale insects are more or less the same shape but flatter. When a plant is infested, the so-called 'honeydew', a sticky substance secreted by the scale insect, appears on or under the leaves. This substance is usually seen before the actual scale insects are noticed. However, it is not too late to do something about them.

To combat these pests, use a piece of cotton wool soaked in methylated spirits and wipe every leaf. The bottom of the leaves, particularly along the main veins, should be thoroughly treated. For places that are difficult to get to, use a brush dipped in methylated spirits and dab the scale insects with this. This should also be repeated two or three times at intervals of 10–14 days. Badly infested plants lose their leaves. In this case the best solution is to cut back the plant and thoroughly clean the remaining parts.

WOOLLY APHIS

The woolly aphis protects itself with a covering of white flakes. It is often found on buds and in leaf axillae and can be combated in the same way as scale insects.

ROOT APHIS

When plants cultivated indoors are repotted, you may notice that the outside of the clump of roots is covered with white specks. When this white stuff is removed, an aphid will be found inside feasting on the sap from the roots. These aphids are difficult to destroy without extremely poisonous preparations. However, if you make sure that the plant is kept moist and is regularly fed with artificial fertilizer, it will probably recover. If the infestation is very bad, the answer may be to take cuttings. Throw away the old plant, and disinfect the pots with boiling soda water.

Root aphis is very rarely found in plants cultivated in the garden.

WHITEFLY

Whitefly is rather difficult to control indoors without the use of very toxic preparations. These small insects feed on the juices in the leaf so that it turns yellow and drops off. They lay numerous eggs on the underside of the leaves. In some cases it helps to cut back the affected plant and remove the remaining leaves, but it does not always work. Recently, yellow sheets of plastic designed to combat whiefly have come onto the market. These have been sprayed with a special preparation, which attracts these insects so that they become stuck. This environmentally friendly remedy is a very satisfactory solution.

ROOTWORMS AND OTHER EELWORMS

These worms, which are hardly visible with the naked eye, feed on healthy roots, living on the sap contained in them. Some cause small or large lumps on the roots, which you will notice when you repot the plant. They can be combated with extremely toxic preparations, but these are only used in nurseries. As in the case of the root aphis, the plant will survive if it is given plenty of fertilizer. Otherwise, try to take cuttings from the plants and then burn the original plants or throw them into the dustbin with the pots.

RED SPIDER MITE

This mite looks like a little spider and spins small webs on the undersides of leaves to protect itself. It feeds on the sap in the cells so that the leaves turn brown. In general, the red spider mite is difficult to destroy. Plants become infected as a result of dry air. This can be prevented by spraying regularly. The red spider mite also intensely dislikes cold water, so it is a good idea to put the infested plants under a cold shower once a week, making sure that the undersides of the leaves are sprayed.

THRIPS

Thrips are striped creatures, one to several millimetres long. They feed on the sap in leaf cells, particularly on the upperside of the leaf, causing a silvery-grey shine. The disease is fairly easy to control. Treat as described for aphids.

INSECTS WHICH FEED ON PLANTS

These are the insects which devour plants, such as caterpillars, woodlice, and slugs.

CATERPILLARS

As they are usually quite large, these creatures are fairly easy to catch. You often become aware of their presence because of their large, brown droppings, which fall next to the plant or on the windowsill. Take a good look among the leaves and you will usually find them fairly quickly. If this does not work, put the plant in a bucket of water overnight so that the soil is covered. This method is particularly successful for caterpillars which are usually active at night, when they feed on the leaves, but hide in the soil around the roots in the daytime. The next day the caterpillars will float to the surface, or be concealed among the leaves, where they will soon come out of hiding if you look for them or shake the plant.

WOODLICE, SLUGS AND EARWIGS

You may be surprised that these three different creatures are grouped together under the same heading, but all three feed on the young soft parts of the plant

and all three are equally easy to catch. Cut a potato lengthways and hollow it out. Then place half the potato with the cut side facing down on the soil in the pot. The creatures will crawl underneath and can be very simply collected in this way. It is even better to use half a pressed grapefruit (though not an orange). As soon as the grapefruit skin starts to rot, replace it with a new one.

SCIARA FLY

These small black flies appear particularly in pot plants if the soil is rich in humus, which is often the case when the plant is replanted. Although they do not do any direct damage, they can be very tiresome flying about. One solution is to use a vapona strip—the latest type, which is no longer dangerous. This type of strip can prevent all sorts of problems, as it will also combat thrips and red spider mites.

EARTHWORMS

Although these creatures which live in the soil do no damage at all, they can be a problem in pots, when they push the soil upwards. Place the pot under water overnight and the worm will appear and you can remove it. However, in the garden, worms are essential. They help to decompose plant remnants as well as aerating the soil by digging underground passages.

Fungal diseases

Fungi appear when it is damp. Some plants are extremely susceptible to particular fungi, and it is not always easy to combat them. In the first instance, it is advisable to make sure that when you water indoor plants which are sensitive to fungi, you do not wet the leaves. In addition, it is important that the leaves of plants which are grown outside have a chance to dry after they have been watered. Good ventilation is essential, so avoid putting plants too close together. The same also applies to plants in the greenhouse, where ventilation should be checked every day.

MILDEW

Mildew is one of the most common fungal diseases. In addition to the general preventative measures described above, you can apply sulphur powder to the leaves of a plant infected with mildew, which will stop the disease spreading. It is advisable to spray vulnerable plants with sulphur powder from time to time, as it can prevent the disease.

RUST

This disease is very common in some plants, such as Pelargoniums, during wet summer months. However, on the whole the plants mentioned in the Bible are not sensitive to this disease. Once a plant is infected with rust it is usually too late. You will see round, reddish-brown circles with a diameter of 5 to 15 mm on the undersides of the leaves. In the same place on the uppersides, the leaf will have yellowish circles. If the disease is caught at an early stage, it may be sufficient to remove the affected leaves. Do this very carefully, as the spores from the reddish-brown circles easily disperse to settle on other leaves and will proliferate again. When a plant has been affected too seriously, cut it back, remove all the leaves, and burn it. If the bare plant is kept in drier conditions, another outbreak of the disease can be prevented.

Other symptoms

LOSS OF LEAVES

Plants which are grown in pots or tubs may lose leaves if they are given too much water. This is easy to check by taking the plant out of the pot. If the soil is too wet, it will have an unpleasant smell, and for a few weeks the plant should not be watered. In most cases the roots will already have partly rotted away, so cut them back to save the plant. Leaves may also be lost if the plant is too dry. In this case, place the plant with its pot in a bucket of water until it stops bubbling. After this it will not be necessary to water the plant for several days.

In some cases plants outside in the garden also have too much water. Usually this means that soil drainage is inadequate, and the water cannot drain away. In this case you can solve the problem by digging the soil so that it is less compacted.

CHLOROSIS

Chlorosis is a deficiency disease which happens when a plant cannot absorb enough iron from the soil. This problem can usually be solved with a simple remedy. Take a few rusty nails and soak them in water. After a while a brown sediment will form, which can be diluted with water and poured around a plant suffering from chlorosis. Repeat this once or twice at intervals of several weeks.

PESTICIDES

Various different brands of pesticides are available from garden shops. Many of these are not toxic and are therefore ideal to use indoors or in the garden. However, there are more toxic than non-toxic pesticides. Fortunately the former are usually difficult for the amateur gardener to purchase. The packaging always indicates how dangerous the preparation is, so read it first before you buy. This also applies to the instructions: read them first, before use. The remedies for combating diseases described here have been kept as simple as possible. In addition, you can prepare non-toxic remedies yourself.

CHRYSANTHEMUM CORONARIUM VAR. DISCOLOR

Acacia

Scientific name:	Acacia tortilis (Forsk.) Hayne
Family name:	Leguminosae
Natural habitat:	tropical Africa, Arabia
English name:	acacia
Biblical name:	acacia wood

They made the altar of incense out of acacia wood. It was square, a cubit long and a cubit wide, and two cubits high . . .
EXODUS 37:25

Between 750 and 800 species of the genus *Acacia* have been identified. They are found in tropical and subtropical countries and are particularly common in Africa and Australia.

The family name is derived from the Greek word *Akakia*, 'a thorny tree'. The tree most people know as the acacia is *Robinia pseudoacacia*, and though it belonging to the same family, Leguminosae, it does not really have anything to do with the genus *Acacia*. In Israel only five species are indigenous, and of these only *Acacia tortilis* subsp. *raddiana* produces good timber. Most *Acacia* species develop into large trees. They include both evergreen and deciduous varieties.

About 300 species have the pseudo-leaves or leaf branches (phylocladia) characteristic of this family. These are twigs which look like leaves and can easily be seen in the young tree, particularly in saplings. Other species have thorns, which can in some cases be enormous. There are also hollow thorns, which initially serve as leaf supports, though they are inhabited by ants at a later stage. *Acacia sphaerocephala* and *A. spaldicigera* are good examples of this.

In return for their home in the tree's thorns, ants help to keep it free of pests. In order to attract an ant colony the plant forms so-called 'ant lobes' at the ends of the leaves.

Many acacias grow in extremely dry or arid regions, such as India and North Africa. They have numerous thorns for protection against being eaten by animals, for which they are often the only meagre source of food. Nevertheless, the branches are still considered a delicacy, especially by chameleons. These creatures seem to have tongues made of leather, for they do not appear to take any notice at all of the sharp and extremely hard thorns.

Flowering acacias can be extremely beautiful. Some varieties are of horticultural interest because their flowers can be cut and sold in florists as 'mimosa'. The main variety to produce these spring flowers is *Acacia dealbata*. This tree's pod-shaped fruit is very striking; in some cases the pods are extremely long. When the fruit is ripe, it bursts open. The splendid, usually shiny black seeds which are revealed are often surrounded by a striking orange or red 'umbilical cord' *(Aryllus)*. This ornamental feature attracts creatures which help to disperse the seeds.

Within the large *Acacia* genus there are several varieties which are the source of important and valuable products. In the strong winds which are frequent during periods of drought the branches and trunk of *Acacia senegal* secrete large quantities of resin which is traded as gum arabic. The bark and pods of other varieties produce tannin, while others provide high quality wood which is carefully collected by the local population to be used as fuel. The wood is also burned to produce high-quality charcoal.

The acacia is mentioned several times in the Old Testament, particularly in the book of Exodus, and especially in connection with the construction of the tabernacle and the ark of the covenant. In those days the few varieties of *Acacia* which grew in the desert were the only trees to produce wood which was suitable for carpentry. As a result of the dry and windy weather the trees grew extremely slowly, and most only reached the maximum height of 5–8 metres after a long time. Many trees never grew this tall, but acquired a characteristic shape flattened on one side through exposure to the elements. Thus they provided shelter in the night or during sandstorms and other bad weather conditions to shepherds, caravans and other travellers. It was precisely because the tree grew so slowly that its wood was particularly hard. In later periods its beautiful orange-red colour made it very popular for marquetry work in beautiful chests and other furniture, and the Egyptians had used the wood many years before for their sarcophagi.

In some parts of the Holy Land acacias were so common that in the Bible their name is linked to a particular region or place. Numbers 25:1 refers to the place Shittim, as does Micah 6:5. Numbers 33:49 refers to Abelshittim, and Joel 3:18 to the Valley of Shittim. These place names are derived from the Hebrew word *Shittah*, which means acacia (plural: *Shittim*).

GROWING TIPS

Acacia armata can only be grown indoors in temperate climates. Others can be grown in tubs and treated like other frost-tender shrubs. This means that they should be grown outside during the summer months and moved to a cool place with a minimum temperature of 5° C during the winter. At these low temperatures and in the short hours of daylight which prevail during the winter months, growth will more or less come to a standstill. The amount of water given to the plants should also be kept to a minimum. Just give enough water to make sure that the soil in the pot does not dry out altogether. In early spring you can repot the plant if necessary, or place it in a new tub and gradually start to give more water. During the growing period the plants generally need a great deal of moisture, and some artificial fertilizer can be added to the water every two or three weeks. If they are well looked after, the plants may be covered in spring with the well-known downy mimosa flowers.

It is possible to buy young plants of the different varieties, or you can grow them yourself from seed. If you are interested in doing this, refer to the section on raising plants from seed.

ACACIA TORTILIS

Acanthus

Scientific name: Acanthus syriacus Boiss
Family name: Acanthaceae
Natural habitat: northern Africa, the Orient
English name: acanthus
Biblical name: underbrush

They brayed among the bushes and huddled in the underbrush.
JOB 30:7

The family name Acanthaceae is derived from the old Greek plant name *Akanthos. Akantha* means thorn or thistle, and the name undoubtedly refers to the thorny, dentate leaves. The plant referred to in the Bible quotation is *Acanthus syriacus,* which is very common in Mediterranean countries.

The leaf, especially the leaf of *Acanthus spinosus,* plays a very important role in art. The motif was commonly used as an ornamental design in architecture and furniture making. It was first used in the Near East and then developed by the Greeks and Romans, who used it particularly to decorate the capitals of Corinthian pillars. The motif is hardly found again in the later Byzantine, Romanesque and Gothic styles, but in the Renaissance and the subsequent classical styles, it was again widely used in decoration. It is not possible to say with great certainty whether the leaf of the acanthus was the original model. Many other plants with similarly shaped leaves which grow in Mediterranean countries, such as various types of thistles, could also have been used.

Nowadays, approximately fifty different varieties of *Acanthus* are known. These grow not only in Mediterranean regions, but also in the tropical and sub-tropical areas of Asia and Africa.

Because most varieties are not very hardy in winter, or not hardy at all, it is only possible to grow a small number of varieties outside in the garden in temperate climates. *Acanthus mollis* is a variety which does thrive in cooler climates. If the plant is well-covered during the cold winter months, for example with a thick layer of fallen leaves, it will grow back more beautifully every year and flower even more profusely. When it flowers in our gardens, *Acanthus mollis* reaches a height of approximately 75–100cm It is by no means rare in damp places in southern Europe, where it will often be seen by the side of shady, chalky railway embankments. The tough flower stalks, which appear towards the end of May, continue to be decorative until about August.

Light mauve blooms 3–5cm long, which resemble labiates, grow between the thorny, purple, dentate bracts which are arranged around the stalk.

When the last flower at the top of the stalk has finished flowering, the first large fruits at the bottom of the stalk are already visible. They each contain seeds 2–4mm long which are forcefully ejected as soon as they are quite ripe, as is true for many Acanthaceae.

GROWING TIPS
It is best to grow the large black seeds, approximately

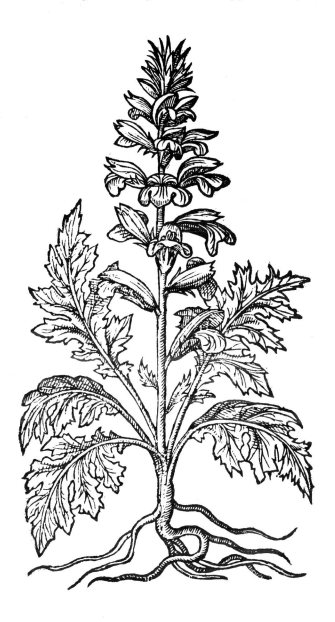

8–10mm long and 3–5mm wide, indoors in mid- to late spring. To encourage germination, it is a good idea to soak the seeds in lukewarm water for 24 hours before sowing them. Place the swollen seeds in a pot filled with plain garden soil or peat. Finally, firmly press down and cover with a layer of soil approximately 12mm deep. Provided the seeds are not too old, the first seedlings with thick seed leaves will appear within a month. It is only when the first leaves are clearly visible that the seedlings can be replanted into separate pots.

Leave them there until the risk of night frost has passed. Then they can be planted outside in their permanent position. However, it is better to keep them in their pots for another year, so you can protect them against frosts. This will make it necessary to repot them into larger pots.

Acanthus plants develop best in a rich, rather chalky soil which should be moist but not too wet. Plant them 50–75cm apart, so that they do not become overcrowded later on when they have developed as fully grown plants.

CAPITAL OF A PILLAR IN WHICH THE ACANTHUS LEAF HAS BEEN USED AS A MOTIF

Calamus

Scientific name: Acorus calamus L.
Family name: Araceae
Natural habitat: Europe, Asia and North America
English name: calamus
Biblical name: cassia

Then the Lord said to Moses, 'Take the following fine spices:
500 shekels of liquid myrrh, half as much (that is, 250 shekels)
of fragrant cinnamon, 250 shekels of fragrant cane, 500
shekels of cassia . . .'
EXODUS 30:22–23

It may come as a surprise to learn that a plant from the lands of the Bible grows successfully in cooler areas, including some of the more northerly countries of Europe. However, calamus *(Acorus calamus)* now grows abundantly over a wide area. As the root stocks of the plant are very fragrant and can be used in many different ways, it was imported and then spread to grow wild on a large scale. An arum (Araceae), it is often seen on the banks of ditches and in marshy regions. Nowadays it is found throughout Europe, Asia and North America.

At first sight a fully grown plant does not closely resemble the arum family. The tall, stiff leaves (up to approximately 120cm long) look a bit like those of the yellow flag which is also found in wet, marshy areas. It is only when both plants are flowering that you can clearly see the difference. Unlike many of the other members of its family, the calamus does not have striking flowers. The genus *Acorus* is in fact one of the more primitive representatives of the Araceae family with regard to the composition of its flowers. The sheathing leaf (or spathe), which is present in most of the varieties of this family as a sheath around the spadix, is entirely absent from the calamus. Instead, the spadix grows approximately 13cm from the root pointing straight out from the flower stalk, which, as it has no sheath, is indistinguishable from a normal leaf. Moreover, as the flower spike is green, it is not very noticeable. Only when you look for them very carefully will you be able to find the odd spadix, especially during the flowering months of early summer.

One characteristic which distinguishes the calamus from the very similar yellow flag *(Iris pseudacorus)* is the leaf, which is much stronger in the former, growing up straight and rigid. In addition, the edges of the leaves are very curled, particularly at the base. Another clear difference is that the leaves of the calamus release a strong, aromatic smell when they are rubbed, which yellow flag leaves do not.

It is only fairly recently that the calamus has been considered to be an indigenous plant in northern Europe. Its roots were not imported to Europe from Asia Minor until the second half of the sixteenth century. Long before this time, however, the plant was well-known in India and China. For centuries great medicinal properties have been ascribed to the aromatic root stocks, with their unique smell and taste. They were used, amongst other things, as a medicine for gastric complaints, and they were transported via the so-called spice routes and traded in the Holy Land in Bible times. Nowadays the root stocks of the *Calamus* are still widely used in the preparation of various alcoholic beverages, such as, for example, the Dutch gin 'Beerenburg'.

In addition to the common green variety, there is a much more attractive coloured variety: *Acorus calamus* 'Variegatus', which is often planted along the edges of ponds. Apart from this, there is also the much smaller *Acorus gramineus*, which is indigenous in Japan and cultivated here mainly as a pot plant, as well as the varieties of this species, 'Argenteostriatus' (which has vertical white stripes) and 'Aureovariegatus' (which has yellow stripes). The variety 'Pusillus', which is even smaller in every respect, is also available occasionally.

GROWING TIPS

The varieties of *Acorus calamus* and *Acorus gramineus* which are mentioned here are fairly hardy in a temperate climate. They do best in a damp spot, for example, on the banks of a pond. All varieties of calamus, large or small, can easily be propagated by splitting the root stock.

ACORUS CALAMUS 'VARIEGATUS'

Aegilops

Scientific name: Aegilops uniaristata Vis.
Family name: Gramineae
Natural habitat: Europe, the Mediterranean
English name: aegilops
Biblical name: grass

They are like plants in the field, like tender green shoots, like grass sprouting on the housetops, scorched before it grows up.
ISAIAH 37:27

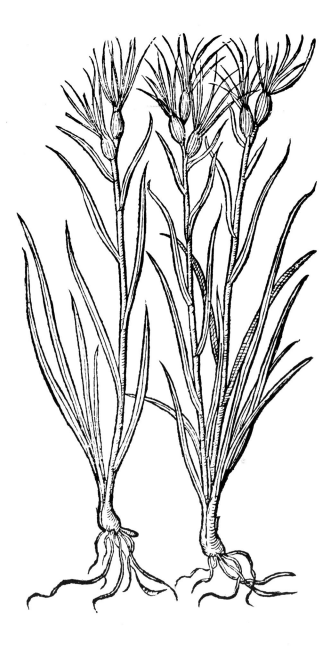

In many types of vegetation, grasses can play quite a dominant role. In fields, the control of different types of grass is an important aspect of cultivation, for where grass is growing, no other crops can develop. Many grass varieties which existed in Bible times can still be found in the Holy Land. One genus which is rather striking when it is in flower is *Aegilops*, which comprises about 25 different types. In temperate climates, a number of these are found growing wild. They are annual grasses which belong to the large family Gramineae. Depending on the variety and on the composition of the soil, they can vary in height from 10–40cm. They have a characteristic cylindrical, bottle-shaped inflorescence which is often twisted and consists of many non-flowering glumes, ending in a needle. Because of this characteristic shape, they are suitable as dried grasses to be combined with other dried flowers.

GROWING TIPS
The seeds of different species of *Aegilops* are not commercially available. It may be possible to collect some seed from the wild, perhaps during a holiday in a Mediterranean country. *Aegilops* often grows abundantly in Mediterranean lands, and is particularly noticeable when ripe because it turns an attractive, straw colour. It will thrive in any soil and can be sown in late spring.

AEGILOPS UNIARISTATA

Corn Cockle

Scientific name: Agrostemma githago L.
Family name: Caryophyllaceae
Natural habitat: Europe
English name: corn cockle
Biblical name: weeds

When the wheat sprouted and formed heads, then the weeds also appeared.
MATTHEW 13:26

In the Bible you will find the word 'tares' or 'weeds' quite a lot. The weed referred to in the texts concerned is usually *Agrostemma githago* or corn cockle. This annual or sometimes biennial plant is a member of the carnation family (Caryophyllaceae) and was very common in arable fields in days gone by, when chemical pesticides were not yet in use and the seeds that were sown still contained many weed seeds. In the past, the corn cockle was often found together with other annual field weeds such as the corn marigold (*Chrysanthemum segetum*), the cornflower (*Centaurea cyanus*), the poppy (*Papaver rhoeas*), Venus's looking glass (*Legousia speculum veneris*), the pimpernel (*Anagallis arvensis*), the pansy (*Viola arvensis*), and the larkspur (*Delphinium consolida*). Some of these plants were known as 'the lilies of the field' in the Bible. The name of the genus *Agrostemma* is derived from the Greek word 'agros' (field) and 'stemma' (crown)—the jewel of the fields. The flowers of this weed which grew in the fields, and was described as the 'field carnation' by Dioscorides, were used to make garlands of flowers.

The plant, which can reach a height of 30–100cm, depending on the type of soil where it is growing, has lance-shaped leaves, tapering to a sharp point and covered in hairs. The single light or dark purple flowers grow on long stalks and appear in midsummer. There is a striking, strongly developed and hairy calyx which swells up into a beautiful spherical ten-ribbed fruit once the flower has been fertilized. When it is ripe, the fruit bursts open at the top and the large black seeds are clearly visible. The stem, the root and especially the seeds contain a toxic substance variously known as Agrostemna-sapotoxine, Githagine, or Agrostemnine. This substance acts as a narcotic and, when it comes into contact with the mucus membrane of the nose, gives rise to violent sneezing. Before grain was cleaned by machine, it often happened that large quantities of cockle seeds would be ground with the grain seeds. The bread baked from this flour had an unpleasant bitter taste and was not at all good to eat. In Southern Limburg in Holland the flower is sometimes called 'broodsbloem' (bread flower) because of this. Symptoms of poisoning, sometimes fatal, have been known to occur after drinking substitute coffee made from grain. Examination showed them to have been caused by the presence of large quantities of cockle seeds.

GROWING TIPS

Corn cockle grows best if you sow the large black seeds in mid to late summer. The plant is not at all fussy about the composition of the soil. It flowers from midsummer onwards. However, it is also possible to sow the seeds in the early spring. The young seedlings are not at all sensitive to frost. As the seedlings have fairly well-developed tap roots, they are difficult to transplant, so if they are too close together, thin them out to approximately 5cm apart. There are several good selections available from seed merchants, such as *Agrostemma githago*, 'Milas', and 'Purple Queen', which have beautifully formed blooms and flower profusely.

AGROSTEMMA GITHAGO 'PURPLE QUEEN'

Onion

Scientific name:	Allium cepa L.
Family name:	Alliaceae
Natural habitat:	Europe
English name:	onion
Biblical name:	onion

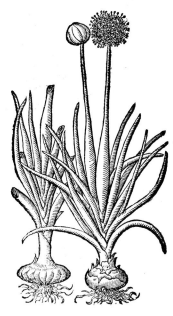

We remember the fish we ate in Egypt at no cost—also the cucumbers, melons, leeks, onions and garlic.

NUMBERS 11:5

The onion as we know it has developed as the result of a long process of selection. The ancestor of the modern onion was undoubtedly a very primitive plant with a significantly lower yield. The *Allium x proliferum (A. fistulosum x. A. cepa)* (syn: *A. cepa* 'Proliferum'; *A. cepa* 'Viviparum'), cultivated in antiquity, was probably the Egyptian onion we know now. This variety produces several small onions with a pungent, rather sharp taste, at the base of each rather thick pipe-like stalk. As well as the onions, the stalks can be eaten, either cooked or raw. Those onions too small for consumption can be replanted.

GROWING TIPS

As *Allium x proliferum* does not produce any seed, you need to collect the bulblets which develop in abundance throughout the growing season at the base of each hollow stalk. These round sets develop in the next growing season. They reproduce fairly rapidly in a warm place in well-manured soil.

The modern varieties of *Allium cepa* are grown from seed in the spring. The crop grows from seed to a fully grown onion in three to four months. The shallot, *Alliumi cepa* var. *ascalonicum* (syn: *Ascolonicum*), is propagated vegetatively in the same way as *Allium x proliferum*.

ALLIUM X PROLIFERUM

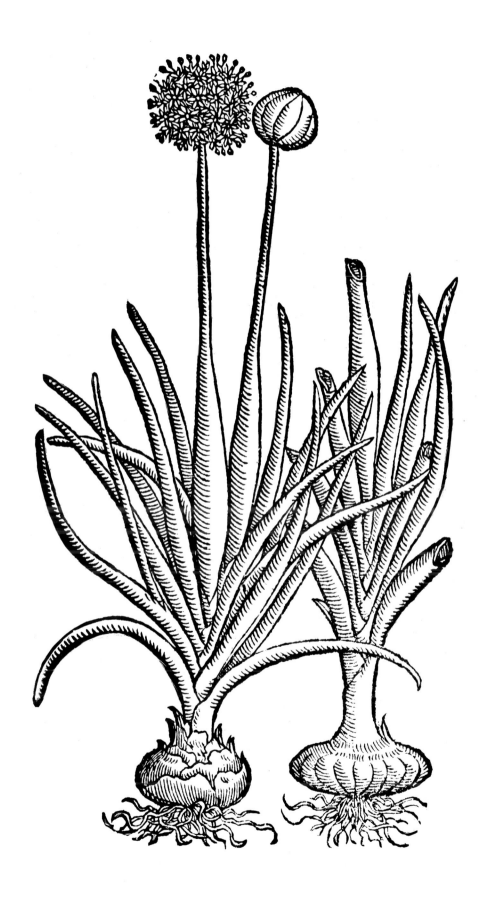

Leek

Scientific name: Allium porrum L.
Family name: Alliaceae
Natural habitat: Europe
English name: leek
Biblical name: leek

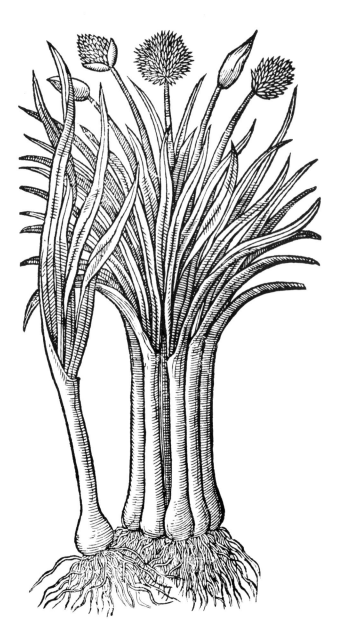

We remember the fish we ate in Egypt at no cost—also the cucumbers, melons, leeks, onions and garlic.

NUMBERS 11:5

The leek, generally grown nowadays as a vegetable, is a plant of unknown origin. The true leek is also unknown in the wild. The varieties cultivated now are the result of cross fertilization and dividing, in which *Allium ampeloprasum* played an important role. Thus the leeks grown in Bible times were very little like the leeks we are familiar with now. At that time they were probably closer to the onion, with edible fleshy leaves surrounding the stalk and forming a short stem. The closest to this now is *Allium porrum* var. *sectivum*, a variety which forms many side shoots like a shallot and is still sometimes pickled in vinegar.

GROWING TIPS

There are dozens of varieties of leeks on the market which can all be grown from seed. They are sown outside in rows in late spring and early summer. As soon as the seedlings have developed into strong plants, plant them out in well-manured soil 15–20cm apart. They should be planted fairly deeply so that they will produce a thick leek later on with a long white lower section. It is also a good idea to bank extra soil around the plants during the growing period. The leek is a biennial plant, which means that it will only flower in the second year after sowing. Although the leaves of a flowering leek are not particularly attractive, the large spherical purple flowers are extremely decorative.

ALLIUM PORRUM

Garlic

Scientific name:	Allium sativum L.
Family name:	Alliaceae
Natural habitat:	Europe
English name:	garlic
Biblical name:	garlic

We remember the fish we ate in Egypt at no cost—also the cucumbers, melons, leeks, onions and garlic.
NUMBERS 11:5

Garlic, *Allium sativum*, is a perennial, bulb-forming plant. Like the onion, this plant was one of the important vegetables of the ancient Hebrews. There is no doubt that it was cultivated in Egypt on a large scale in the time of Moses. Garlic is still one of the most popular vegetables in Mediterranean countries today. It can be eaten either raw, boiled or fried. The bulb itself consists of a number of different segments or cloves, which are closely bound together by thin papery white skins.

GROWING TIPS

Despite the fact that garlic is not completely hardy in temperate climates, the plant can nevertheless be successfully grown out of doors. Plant out the cloves, available from seed merchants, in early summer, in a warm, sunny spot in well-drained fertile soil. Plant them at a depth of 3–4cm. They will develop reasonably throughout the growing season, depending on the weather. Garlic cannot be grown from seed, but is propagated by dividing the bulb and planting out the cloves which compose the fully grown bulb. The chance of a good harvest is best after a warm dry summer. As soon as the leaves start to look as though they are going to wilt, take out the bulbs and dry them out in a dry spot, out of the sun. When the leaves have completely shrivelled, the bulbs can be cleaned and are ready for consumption.

The decorative rocambole, *Allium sativum var. ophioscorodon*, is recommended for planting in the garden. This variety is really hardy in the winter and has striking snake-like flowers. At the height of flowering the plant grows 100–120cm tall, producing first flowers and then little bulbs which can later be planted out separately.

ALLIUM SATIVUM

Aloe

Scientific name: Aloe barbadensis Miller
Family name: Liliaceae
Natural habitat: Madagascar, central and southern
                     Africa
English name: aloe
Biblical name: aloe

---

*Nicodemus bought a mixture of myrrh and aloes, about
seventy-five pounds.*
JOHN 19:39

Of over 300 different varieties of aloe now known, most originated in South Africa. Some of these were originally found in Madagascar, while a small percentage is also indigenous to various Central African countries. At the time that the Bible was written there were only a few varieties in the Holy Land. However, nowadays these plants are very common there, as in other parts of the Mediterranean, and even grow wild in some places. They are all descendants of species which were imported as decorative plants. In addition, many hybrids were produced through cross-pollination, each grower vying to produce the most beautiful flower. It is difficult to say with any certainty which species was referred to in the passage from John 19:39. According to some authors, this could have been *Aloe succotrina*, although this variety was not indigenous to the Holy Land, nor to the island of Socotra, as its name suggests. The first person to use the species name *succotrina* was Dapper in his *Precise Descriptions of the African Regions*, published in Amsterdam in 1668 with a later edition dating from 1676. In his chapter 'The island of Sokotora', he describes the vegetation of the island: 'Large numbers of Sokotorian aloes grew here. These were described by some as succotrina, as though they meant succocitrina, derived from succus and citrus.' The name thus refers in the first instance to the yellow colour of the sap crystals, rather than to the name of the island. However, intensive botanical research has revealed that *Aloe succotrina* is indigenous to South Africa, where it grows in the ravines of the Table Mountain.

It is more likely that *Aloe barbadensis* (syn: *A. vera*) is the variety referred to in the Bible, or perhaps, though less probably, *Aloe perryi* from Socotra. Plants which are now collected under the species name *Aloe barbadensis* were already known in the first century AD and possibly even two thousand years earlier. This species was cultivated in Egypt, where it was used for embalming the dead. It was also commonly planted on graves; this still happens nowadays in countries such as Somalia, Ethiopia and Eritrea. The aloe is not unknown as a medicinal plant. The sap contained in the thick leaves in large quantities has a very bitter taste and acts as a laxative.

According to ancient Egyptian beliefs, this plant had special powers. It is known that in Cairo and in the surrounding area it would be hung above the door of a new house when people moved in, to ensure that they would have a long and fruitful life.

The most important natural habitat of *Aloe barbadensis* is North Africa. This habitat stretches east from Morocco all the way to Egypt. The plant is also found in Palestine, Syria and Greece, and on the islands of Cyprus, Malta and Sicily. Probably this area stretches even further east as far as India, and it seems that this aloe can also be found growing wild in the Cape Verde Islands, in the Canary Islands, and on Madeira. It is fairly certain that the plants were taken by seafaring Spaniards from the Canary Islands to the New World, where they now grow wild in many places, for example on the islands of Barbados, Jamaica and Puerto Rico, and in countries such as Mexico, Peru, Venezuela and Bolivia.

GROWING TIPS

Aloes are easy to grow. They can give a great deal of pleasure, particularly if they can be brought into a frost-free, light and cool place in winter and planted out in the garden during the summer months. If they are grown in full sunlight, most varieties will flower profusely. In general they flower in spring, but there are also varieties which flower during the summer.

In order to grow beautiful, well-formed plants, the soil should not be too rich in nutrients, or the plants will be weak. It could be composed, for example, of equal parts of compost and soil. Aloes can be propagated from seed, from runners or by taking cuttings

Rose of Jericho

Scientific name:	Anastatica hierochuntica L.
Family name:	Cruciferae
Natural habitat:	Africa to Arabia and Iran
English name:	rose of Jericho
Biblical name:	tumbleweed

Make them like tumbleweed, O my God, like chaff before the wind.

PSALM 83:13

open

There are two plants which could be the plant referred to in the Bible by the term 'tumbleweed'. In both cases they die away to leave dry plant fibres which are easily uprooted by the wind and blown through the sand of the desert. The thistle *Grundelia tournefortii*, which belongs to the family Compositae, is the larger, reaching a height of 100–150cm The 'true' Bible rose of Jericho, *Anastatica hierochuntica*, is much smaller: the largest specimens reach a height of about 30cm.

Over the course of the centuries the name 'rose of Jericho' has become an idea in in itself. Hundreds of years ago, the 'true' rose of Jericho was brought to Europe as a curiosity. It was not until later that the 'false' rose of Jericho was introduced and was enthusiastically sold at markets and annual fairs. The fact that the seemingly dead ball of stems could be brought back to life when it was put in water aroused general astonishment and disbelief.

In the course of history some confusion has arisen about which plant can be called the 'real' rose of Jericho. As is often the case, the same popular name has been given to different plants. The two species which are described as the 'rose of Jericho' are most easily distinguished by using the adjectives 'true' and 'false'.

The 'true' rose of Jericho: *Anastatica hierochuntica* (Cruciferae) grows wild in an area stretching from Morocco to Iran. During the dry season, when the seeds of this plant ripen, the leaves fall off and the twigs roll up and turn in on themselves. In this way the plant shrivels up into a small, round ball. When it is uprooted during a storm, this dry spherical skeleton rolls through the desert until it reaches a moist place, where it unfolds. The seeds are released, germinate quickly, and in a short while develop into fully grown plants.

The 'false' rose of Jericho: *Selaginella lepidophylla* is a plant with the same characteristics as the 'true' rose of Jericho. It, too, opens when it is put in water, but basically it has no connection with the 'true' rose of Jericho. The plant was originally found in Central America from Texas to El Salvador, and belongs to the *Selaginella* genus (family Selaginellaceae). Varieties of Selaginella, also known as mosses, are sometimes grown as pot plants, and are particularly used to fill small plant bowls.

In temperate climates the 'true' rose of Jericho is virtually unavailable, but the 'false' variety is sometimes sold. Imported from Central America, the plant can no longer be revived after its long sea journey and an even longer period in a warehouse. It may seem to revive when it is placed in water, but it is not possible to make it grow again. If the dry skeleton is kept moist for a long time, it can become entirely covered with a layer of green algae, which gives the false impression that it is growing.

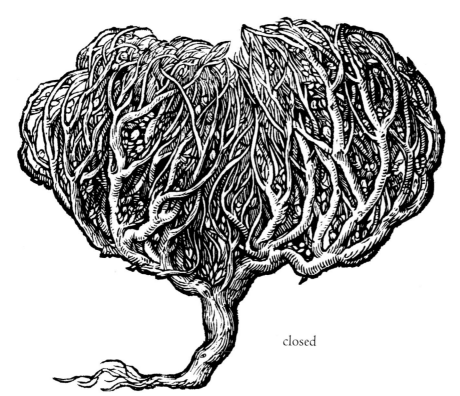

closed

GROWING TIPS

The 'true' rose of Jericho is an annual plant which is actually very easy to grow in the garden the summer months. The main problem is getting the seeds: as the plant is not particularly attractive it is rarely grown commercially, and is therefore seldom found in botanical collections. However, if seeds are available, you can sow them in the open ground in early summer. You need a patch of poor soil, and should dig it over and level it well in advance. The plant germinates quickly, and rapidly develops to the flowering stage. However, it is unlikely that you will succeed in growing a good, compact specimen, usually because garden soil contains too many nutrients and is too moist for these desert plants.

ANASTATICA HIEROCHUNTICA

Anemone

Scientific name:	Anemone coronaria L.
Family name:	Ranunculaceae
Natural habitat:	Mediterranean area
English name:	anemone
Biblical name:	lily

Consider how the lilies grow. They do not labour or spin. Yet I tell you, not even Solomon in all his splendour was dressed like one of these.

LUKE 12:27

Lilies are often mentioned in the Bible. In fact, the name is often used to indicate a large group of different plants which flower at more or less the same time, with beautiful, striking blooms.

One of the plants which was undoubtedly one of these 'lilies of the field' (as some translations render the verse in Luke) is the anemone, *Anemone coronaria*. In contrast with most other species, this plant has a bulbous root stock which lasts from one season to the next and comes back to life in March or April if there has been sufficient rainfall during the autumn and winter. Not only do the bulbs start to grow again, but at the same time many of the seeds start to germinate. For a very short period the arid regions of the Holy Land can be transformed into exuberant landscapes of flowers. However, because of the lack of rain throughout the rest of the year, this period of flowering quickly comes to an end.

GROWING TIPS

In temperate climates, *Anemone coronaria* is not only commonly and popularly used for cut flowers but can also be very easily grown in the garden. The small bulbs grown from seed, which are known as corms, are available everywhere. Over the years many selections have been developed in different colours, including double varieties. For late summer blooms, plant them in a sunny spot in the spring. If you want them to flower in early spring, plant them in the autumn. You should protect the corms from frost by covering them during the winter with leaves or conifer twigs. They can be left in place for many years, provided the soil is well drained and they are fed with manure at regular intervals. You can propagate these plants from seed or by dividing the corms without any significant problems.

ANEMONE CORONARIA

Dill

Scientific name: Anethum graveolens L.
Family name: Umbelliferae
Natural habitat: Europe, northern Africa, southwest Asia and India
English name: dill
Biblical name: caraway

When he has levelled the surface, does he not sow caraway and scatter cumin?

ISAIAH 28:25

Dill *(Anethum graveolens)* has been used since ancient times as a kitchen herb. The flowers and seed cases are used for preserving gherkins, cocktail onions and sauerkraut. The young, finely branched leaves and stalks can be used to season fresh tomato, lettuce, cucumber, and in sauces served with dishes of meat and fish. However, the finely chopped leaves should not be cooked with the dish, as cooking causes it to lose its delicate aromatic taste. This also happens if the leaf and the unripe fruit coronas are dried, though the ripe seeds do retain their taste after being dried.

Dill is still regarded as a useful medicinal plant. It was widely used in the past in this way, for example, in the form of dill water for the treatment of gastric and intestinal complaints. This medicine was prepared by distillation and contained a lot of essential oils. Like other seed herbs, such as fennel, coriander, and aniseed, dill has a 'warming' effect when served as a tea. This is soothing for the stomach and intestines and can also be used to treat colds, infections and other complaints.

Dill belongs to the family Umbelliferae and is indigenous to Mediterranean countries. Depending on the composition of the soil and the amount of rainfall, this annual plant can grow to a height of 2.5m. It is not unfamiliar in temperate climates, and is increasingly grown for its flowers, as well as for use in the kitchen. The cut flowers are used in mixed bouquets.

GROWING TIPS

Dill is sown in lines or simply scattered in the soil in early spring. It is not fussy about soil. The seeds will germinate after approximately two or three weeks. If necessary, thin out the seedlings about 10cm apart when they have appeared. This will encourage the plants to grow better. It is not a good idea to transplant dill because of its strongly developed tap root. For optimal growth a sunny spot is essential. Although dill can actually grow to a height of 2.5m in good conditions, its usual height is between 100 and 150cm.

ANETHUM GRAVEOLENS

Bulrush

Scientific name:	Arundo donax L.
Family name:	Gramineae
Natural habitat:	southern Europe, central and southern Asia
English name:	bulrush
Biblical name:	reed

On whom are you depending, that you rebel against me? Look now, you are depending on Egypt, that splintered reed of a staff, which pierces a man's hand and wounds him if he leans on it! Such is Pharaoh king of Egypt to all who depend on him.
2 KINGS 18:20–21

A reed swayed by the wind and the staff mentioned in this text undoubtedly refer to *Arundo donax*, also known as the bulrush. This genus, which belongs to the grass family (Gramineae) and is found in tropical and sub-tropical regions, comprises twelve different species, of which *Arundo donax* is the best known.

It is very common in Mediterranean countries and is found particularly on river banks or in wet and marshy regions. It is a giant grass which can reach a height of some 6m when fully grown and crowned with its flowering plume. The hard, thick, hollow stalks are rather like bamboo. They grow in sections and are between 3 and 8cm thick. They have many different uses. For example, they are used as fishing rods, for making screens and fences and as plant supports. The stalks can be split and plaited to make matting. All sorts of garden furniture in Mediterranean countries have canopies made of this sort of reed. Bulrushes are perennials, forming thick, strangely-shaped root stocks underground, which are often found in a river bed or washed up on the beach after the plants have died off.

GROWING TIPS

Although *Arundo donax* is not a hardy plant in temperate climates, you can grow this plant all the year round if you provide adequate winter protection. The variegated form, *Arundo donax* 'Variegata', is particularly suitable because of its beautiful green and white striped leaves. In warm summers the plant can grow to a considerable height if it is grown in a warm, sunny spot in fertile, well-drained soil. However, during cold winters the parts above the ground will freeze. Remove this dead growth in spring, and new shoots will develop as the temperature rises. As the plant does not form any seed in temperate parts of the world, propagate it by dividing the root stock.

ARUNDO DONAX

Milk Vetch

Scientific name:	Astragalus gummifer Labill.
Family name:	Leguminosae
Natural habitat:	Syria
English name:	milk vetch
Biblical name:	spices

... Take them down to the man as a gift—a little balm and a little honey, some spices and myrrh, some pistachio nuts and almonds.

GENESIS 43:11

In arid regions plants usually grow very slowly because of the lack of rainfall. This stimulates the development of volatile oils and many people who have walked through *maquis* will recall the fragrant spicy smell of it.

Some plants produce gum or resin when they are damaged, and this is often used for medicinal purposes or as a perfume. In addition to some species from the genera *Cistus*, *Commiphora*, and *Ferula*, other gum-producing plants include *Astragalus massiliensis* (syn. *A. tragacantha*) and *A. gummifer*.

The genus *Astragalus*, which comprises almost 2,000 different species and belongs to the family Leguminosae, is found throughout the world, particularly in dry regions. It includes both perennial herbs and shrubs. The latter include several resin- or gum-producing plants which grow on arid mountain slopes such as those in the Holy Land (Song of Solomon 8:14). These species grow into fairly large, cushion-shaped plants, approximately 50cm high, which are quite impenetrable because of their many branches and thorns.

The thorns appear when the individual leaves on the composite leaf stalk have fallen. The main vein which remains behind grows into a strong, light yellowish thorn, and several yellowish-white hairs develop between these thorns. White or yellow axillary flowers shaped like butterflies appear in the growing tips, together forming bunches, ears or heads. The resin or gum, known as tragacanth, comes from the roots and is traded in the form of strings. These swell up in water and turn into a sticky, slimy substance. It is used in the pharmaceutical industry, for making suspensions and for binding powdery substances. Nowadays, Turkey is the largest producer in the world, with a production of over 3,500 tons a year.

ASTRAGALUS MASSILIENSIS

GROWING TIPS

Both *Astragalus gummifer* and *A. massiliensis* can easily be grown outside in temperate climates if they are protected to some extent against the worst winter cold. They require a very well-drained soil which is not too rich in nutrients, and a spot in full sunlight. They do best in a rockery. Protect the plants against too much rain in winter by placing a pane of glass over them. Over the years they will grow into shrubs which flower profusely during the summer months.

Propagate the plant by taking cuttings. These take a long time to take root so it is a good idea to use rooting powder. Young plants can also be grown from seed.

Tree Purslane

Scientific name: Atriplex halimus L.
Family name: Chenopodiaceae
Natural habitat: southern Europe
English name: tree purslane
Biblical name: salt herbs

In the brush they gathered salt herbs, and their food was the root of the broom tree.
JOB 30:4

The origin of the Greek word for this plant means 'salted' or 'from the sea.' This could be due to the fact that a number of these plants are very resistant to salt and sea winds. This is characteristic of many species of the plant, a number of which are found in Mediter-ranean countries. The species name of *Atriplex halimus* is a further indication of this, as it is based on the Latin equivalent of the Greek 'halimos' (hals, halos: salt).

Most species of *Atriplex* are annuals, but *Atriplex halimus* develops as a small perennial shrub. The branches are covered with silvery-grey, oval or diamond-shaped overlapping leaves. The greenish flowers grow in plumes and develop a characteristic yellowish-green colour when they have formed fruit. The leaves, which are edible, have a rather salty taste. Other species which might have been referred to in the Bible text above are *Atriplex rosea* and *A. tatarica*.

GROWING TIPS
Atriplex halimus is a plant which has traditionally been grown in the temperate climate of northern Europe since 1594. This species is eminently suitable for cultivation in sunny spots in coastal areas. It will grow less prolifically in a soil that is poor in nutrients, but elsewhere the plants can develop to a considerable size and need regular pruning to keep them in check. You can propagate it either from seed or by taking cuttings.

ATRIPLEX
HALIMUS

Oats

Scientific name: Avena sterilis L.
Family name: Gramineae
Natural habitat: southern Europe
English name: oats
Biblical name: grass

And he directed the people to sit down on the grass.
MATTHEW 14:19

References in the Bible to grass do not merely indicate the grasses that we know now. Other green herb-like plants also fall under the Bible term 'grass', so it is difficult to ascertain precisely which of the hundreds of different grasses which grow in the Holy Land is meant. Because grass, like other weeds, is referred to very frequently in the Bible, a number of the most important and best known varieties of grasses are described later in the book, listed under their scientific names.

Oats, *Avena sterilis,* belonging to the large family of grasses (Gramineae), are abundant throughout the Mediterranean area and can even be found much further north, as an adventive plant. This species of wild oats grows to a height of about 20–80cm, depending on its position and the amount of moisture available.

GROWING TIPS
Like all annual grasses, oats grow very easily from seed and are totally unfussy about soil. If a plant is sown in mid-spring, it will flower profusely in late summer. You can harvest oats when they have flowered and are starting to turn yellow. Hang the plants to dry upside down in a well-ventilated place out of the sun.

AVENA STERILIS

Black Mustard

Scientific name: Brassica nigra (L.) Koch
Family name: Cruciferae
Natural habitat: central and southern Europe
English name: black mustard
Biblical name: mustard

It is like a mustard seed, which a man took and planted in his garden. It grew, became a tree, and the birds of the air perched in its branches.

LUKE 13:19

Despite all the discussion that there has been about the mustard seed in Jesus's parable, experts still cannot agree about the specific plant referred to here. It was probably black mustard *(Brassica nigra).*

Nowadays, varieties of this plant with a rather stunted growth are cultivated for their seed. These plants are easy to process by machine and leave proportionally less waste behind on the land when they have been dried. However, the original *Brassica nigra* referred to in the verses above can reach a height of 1.5m, and sometimes even more in a fertile field. It is not entirely inconceivable that a small seed of black mustard sown in fertile soil in ideal conditions could, in a year, grow into a thick-stemmed plant with so many branches that it would be like a tree, with a height of 3.5m.

Sinapsis alba or white mustard also grows in the Holy Land, though it is less common. It has a similar habit, and it is possible that Jesus was speaking about this

plant. The seeds of both plants are spherical in shape and with a diameter of 1–5mm, they would count as small seeds.

GROWING TIPS

The seeds of the Cruciferae, which include the black and white mustard plants, contain a great deal of oil, which enables them to survive many years of dormancy. If you sow them in spring, the seeds will rapidly germinate. It would be interesting to try and grow as large a plant as possible from one of these seeds in a single season. To do this, place the plant in a sunny spot and feed it generously with organic manure. If the rapidly growing plant is constantly given plenty of water and artificial fertilizer, the results will be astonishing.

BRASSICA NIGRA

Flowering Rush

Scientific name: Butomus umbellatus L.
Family name: Butomaceae
Natural habitat: Europe and Asia
English name: flowering rush
Biblical name: reeds

. . . when out of the river there came up seven cows, sleek and fat, and they grazed among the reeds.
GENESIS 41:2

The 'reeds' referred to in Genesis 41:2 and the 'rushes' referred to in Job 8:11 are probably a collective noun for a number of different marsh plants which grow rather like grasses. As in our own flora, quite a few plants could be concerned here. One of these is the flowering rush, *Butomus umbellatus*, which grows on the banks of the Nile and is found in many other areas throughout the continents of Europe and Asia. It is the one species in its genus, and is classed in a family of its own, Butomaceae. The flowering rush is a perennial plant with long, narrow, pointed leaves which grow from the foot of a cylindrical stem. The umbels are composed of striking pink flowers on long stalks. They vary in height from 0.5 to 1.5m and flower from June to August.

GROWING TIPS

Flowering rushes are indigenous in many parts of Europe, and widely available. You can plant out young plants, sold in garden centres, on the banks of a pond or ditch, where they will quickly develop into large, profusely flowering clumps. Propagate the plants by dividing them.

BUTOMUS
UMBELLATUS

Capers

Scientific name: Capparis spinosa L.
Family name: Capparidaceae
Natural habitat: the Mediterranean
English name: capers
Biblical name: caper-bush

---

*. . . and the grasshopper is weighed down and the caper-bush
loses its tang.*
ECCLESIASTES 12:5

Capers pickled in vinegar are a delicacy. It is surprising
to find out that they are the buds of *Capparis spinosa*. It
comes as another surprise to see the large and extremely
beautiful flowers produced by this plant. It is

indigenous to the Mediterranean countries and forms
part of the Capparidaceae family, growing in dry
regions with a preference for stony ground. The sweet-
smelling flowers open late in the afternoon and remain
open all night, attracting by their scent the moths which
pollinate them. When they have been fertilized, thick
long-ribbed fruits develop, with seeds embedded in
their soft flesh. Creatures which are attracted to eat the
fruit thus help to distribute the seed.

GROWING TIPS

This woody plant is not hardy in cooler climates and is
very difficult to cultivate even in a frost-free sunny
greenhouse. If you plant it in the open ground in a
heated greenhouse, you may succeed in getting it to
flower. It is nevertheless easy to germinate from seed.

CAPPARIS SPINOSA

Thistle

Scientific name: Carthamus glaucus Bieb.
Family name: Compositae
Natural habitat: the Crimea, Egypt, southwest Asia
English name: thistle
Biblical name: thistle

Thorns and thistles will grow up and cover their altars.
HOSEA 10:8

Throughout the Mediterranean, including the Holy Land, there are many different sorts of thistle. The text quoted above refers to all these different thorns and thistles in a single phrase. Apart from some of the thorny species of cornflowers described under *Centaurea calcitrapa*, there are many other species which could be mentioned in this context. One of these is *Carthamus glaucus*, which grows more than 1m tall and has such sharp thorns that if you unexpectedly come into contact with it, you will not forget it in a hurry. The species, which is related to the safflower, *Carthamus tinctorius*, has cruel prickles on its leaves and stalks, which give the bluish-grey tough leaves an even more dangerous appearance.

GROWING TIPS

Although it may not be easy to obtain the seeds, it is certainly worthwhile trying to grow *Carthamus glaucus*. With its large inflorescence and bluish-grey leafy branches, it is an outstanding plant which will best come into its own at the back of a border where it cannot get in anyone's way. Sow the seeds at the end of April or the beginning of May and the plant will grow to a height of 1.5m, depending on moisture levels and the type of soil (although it is not fussy about soil). If you cut the stalks and dry them, the flowers will remain decorative for a long time and can be combined with other striking dried flowers.

CARTHAMUS
GLAUCUS

Safflower

Scientific name: Carthamus tinctorius L.
Family name: Compositae
Natural habitat: Asia Minor and Iran
English name: safflower
Biblical name: saffron

. . . nard and saffron, calamus and cinnamon . . .
SONG OF SONGS 4:14

Safflower, also known as 'poor man's saffron', is an ancient cultivated plant which was originally used for dyeing clothes. In poor countries the petals were also used for colouring foodstuffs, replacing the much more expensive saffron, which comes from the *Crocus sativus*. The safflower, *Carthamus tinctorius*, belongs to the family Compositae and is indigenous to Asia Minor and Iran. It is an annual plant rather like a thistle, and can grow to a height of 50–120cm (depending on the soil) with beautiful orange-yellow or red flowers. Nowadays the cultivation of safflowers for dyes is less important because of the cheaper chemical substitutes that are available. However, safflower is still often sold as a substitute for saffron.

Once when I was on holiday in Tenerife and went on a coach excursion, the driver stopped at a cafe where saffron was sold specially to tourists at an extremely low price, or so the group leader told us with some pride. I examined the product suspiciously, and came to the conclusion that it consisted of the dried petals of the safflower. In the garden behind the cafe there were many *Carthamus tinctorius* plants for yet another harvest of fake saffron. I suspect that despite my protestations, the cafe still serves as a stop for many coachloads of enthusiastic buyers!

GROWING TIPS

You can grow this beautiful plant from seed in cooler climates as well. Seeds are available from any well-stocked seed merchant and should be sown outside in early summer.

There are thirty different known species of the genus *Carthamus*, many of which are very thorny. One of these, *Carthamus glaucus*, is referred to in the Bible under 'thorns and thistles'. In fact, this plant is cultivated in the same way as the previous species. When they are dried, the plants are very suitable for use in mixed bouquets of dried flowers.

CARTHAMUS TINCTORIUS

Cedar of Lebanon

Scientific name: Cedrus libani A. Richard
Family name: Pinaceae
Natural habitat: southwest Asia
English name: cedar of Lebanon
Biblical name: cedar

---

*. . . they will grow like a cedar of Lebanon; planted in the house
of the Lord, they will flourish in the courts of our God.*
PSALM 92:12–13

The cedar of Lebanon, *Cedrus libani*, which has virtually
been eradicated from its original natural habitat, the
mountain slopes of Lebanon, is always a reminder of
the temple of Solomon. This temple, built in about
950 BC, was covered for a large part with the
wonderfully fragrant cedarwood. Tens of thousands of
people were sent up high into the mountains of
Lebanon to cut down the giant trees and bring them
down to the coast. Tied together as rafts, the trunks
were transported southwards by sea to somewhere in
the region of the present-day city of Tel Aviv, and
thence carried inland in the direction of Jerusalem.

The cedar of Lebanon was the noblest, tallest and
most massive tree known to the Israelites at the time.
The trees, which grow to a height of approximately
40m, and their trunks, which can reach a diameter of
about 3m, are an awe-inspiring sight. The young trees
grow more or less in the shape of a pyramid, but over
the years the branches grow more horizontally, giving
the tree its special, remarkable and majestic shape. In
Solomon's time these characteristic trees grew
abundantly in the mountainous areas of the Lebanon,
but because of the large demand for the valuable
cedarwood, fully-grown trees are now extremely rare.
The wood of the cedar of Lebanon was not only valued
for its excellent quality, but also as a symbol of status,
power and dignity. Apart from Solomon, Hiram and
Cyrus, the kings of Assyria and other rulers of
neighbouring countries plundered the mountainous
regions of the Lebanon to acquire the cedarwood
which they used to adorn their palaces.

It took seven years to build the tremendous temple
of Solomon, which had already been started under King
David. The construction of Solomon's private
dwellings and other buildings, including the house of
his wife, Pharoah's daughter, took another thirteen
years. In order to do all this, Solomon first sent 30,000
Israelites serving in the army to the Lebanon to cut

down cedars with King Hiram and his men. Later he
used an entire army, consisting of 3,300 officers and
150,000 workmen. Since that time up to the present—
a period of almost 3,000 years—many people intent
on making a profit have waged a veritable war of
destruction against the green woods of the Lebanon,
without a thought for the consequences. The result was
that the once richly wooded slopes soon fell prey to
erosion and have now assumed the appearance of a
lunar landscape.

Nowadays, cedars are being planted once again in
various places in this part of the world, in an attempt to
recreate the famous woods of the past. It is self-evident
that this is no easy task in this troubled zone. When we
remember how long it takes for a young *Cedrus libani* to
grow to any size at all in more favourable conditions,
with adequate rainfall and good soil, it will be clear that
this attempt to recreate the ancient woods will show
few results in the foreseeable future.

GROWING TIPS
Because of the size to which they grow, cedars are
generally only suitable for large gardens and parks.
Dwarf varieties may be planted in town gardens, and
these are available from well-stocked garden centres.
There are even some varieties that remain small and are
specially cultivated for planting in rockeries. Although
Cedrus libani can also be grown from seed, it will be a
long time before it makes a plant of any size. Moreover,
the young plants are rather sensitive to frost, so that it is
necessary to cover them in winter for the first few years.

The beautifully formed cones are widely used,
particularly as part of Christmas decorations. They
should be picked before they are ripe, while they are
still closed and green, as they will otherwise fall apart.

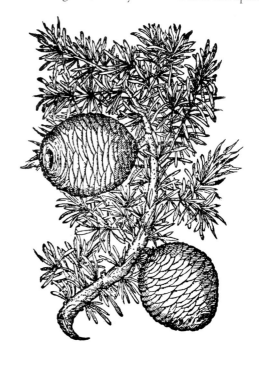

Star Thistle

Scientific name: Centaurea calcitrapa L.
Family name: Compositae
Natural habitat: southern, central and western
    Europe
English name: star thistle
Biblical name: thistle

Because you listened to your wife and ate from the tree about which I commanded you, 'You must not eat of it', cursed is the ground because of you; through painful toil you will eat of it all the days of your life. It will produce thorns and thistles for you.

GENESIS 3:17–18

The Bible refers to 'thorns and thistles' several times. These are a number of different plants belonging to various genera which all produce thorns. In Israel today there are no fewer than 100 different species.

Among these are some that can also be found further afield and could even be included amongst the indigenous flora of northern Europe. The best known and most common of these are Our Lady's thistle and the star thistle. In the countries surrounding the Mediterranean, *Centaurea calcitrapa* (Compositae) is a very common plant. The flowers, and later on, the fruit, are armed with enormous scaly thorns, and the many small flowers which form the head have to find their way through these thorns carefully, without damaging their petals. Although the stems and leaves do not have this sort of protection, the plant is quite safe from animals, which cannot devour so much as a leaf. The dry, hot places where these plants grow, often in very large numbers, can be quite impenetrable to people and animals because of the sharp thorns.

In northern Europe, where the plant grows particularly along the coast, by the roadside and on dikes, it is less heavily armed with thorns than the varieties further south. This is because the soil in which the plants grow here is usually more nutritious, and particularly because the rainfall is much higher. The plants also grow much faster and are much taller—up to a maximum of 60–70cm. When they are grown in rich garden soil they can be even more robust: up to 90–100cm tall.

It will be clear that the plants which are found in the countries of the south growing in seemingly bone-dry soil are much more typical than the specimens found in the cooler parts of Europe.

GROWING TIPS

It is precisely because of its sharp thorns that the star thistle is an interesting plant to grow. In cooler climates it can easily be treated as an annual. It is essential to plant it where it will catch the most sun. The plant is totally unfussy about soil, but the fewer nutrients the soil contains and the drier it is, the smaller and thornier the plant will grow.

CENTAUREA CALCITRAPA

Carob

Scientific name: Ceratonia siliqua L.
Family name: Leguminosae
Natural habitat: Mediterranean area as far as Portugal
English name: carob
Biblical name: pods

He longed to fill his stomach with the pods that the pigs were eating, but no-one gave him anything.
LUKE 15:16

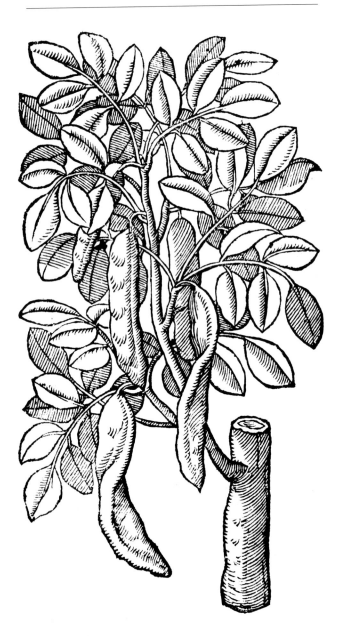

Ceratonia belongs to the family Leguminosae. It is a 'monotypical' genus, which means that only one species is known: *Ceratonia siliqua,* carob. In some Mediterranean areas with sparse plant cover, these evergreen trees, which can grow to a maximum height of 10m, can constitute the most important vegetation. Older specimens develop into beautiful knotted trees, which always provide cool and pleasant shade because of the dense foliage. The heartwood is extremely hard and reddish purple in colour. The flowers are rather strange; small and without a corolla. They are either male (with five stamens) or female (with one pistil). They usually appear on the old wood in early spring or late autumn. This phenomenon, by which flowers grow directly on the trunk, is known as caulinary flowering.

The fruits, which are brown and pod-shaped, contain a great deal of starch, and have a sweet taste because they are 40–50 per cent sugar. In countries where *Ceratonia siliqua* is very common, the leathery pods are gathered in the autumn and most are processed for cattle food. In the neighbourhood of a factory where these pods are being processed, you will notice the pleasant, sweet smell, which can carry several miles. In addition, *eau de vie* is distilled from the fruit. This is sold in Portugal, for example, as 'Aguardente de Alfarroba'. It is very cheap and is sold in virtually any supermarket. The fruit is also used for making syrup and as an aromatic ingredient in the tobacco industry.

The rather large brown seeds, which virtually all have the same weight, were used by the ancient Greeks to weigh gold. The unit for weighing gold, the carat, is derived from this. Nowadays the carat is still used. It has been given a value of 200mg, and may only be used for the trade in pearls and gems. Ordinary metric weights are used in the gold trade, and carats serve only to indicate the gold content; for example, pure gold has a rating of 24 carats.

GROWING TIPS
The carob tree is very easy to grow from seed, which you could obtain, for example, from a holiday in a Mediterranean country. Sow it in a pot filled with moist peat and covered with a plastic bag, and place in a warm spot on the windowsill. The seed will only germinate after 3–6 months, and may take even longer. After this, development is fairly rapid. You can encourage the plant's growth by regularly repotting it. It can be moved outdoors into the garden during the summer, and in a sunny spot it will gather strength for the subsequent winter months. In the winter it should be kept in a cool but frost-free place. Apart from this, treat the plant in the same way as other conservatory plants.

CERATONIA SILIQUA

Judas Tree

Scientific name: Cercis siliquastrum L.
Family name: Leguminosae
Natural habitat: Mediterranean area as far as eastern Bulgaria
English name: Judas tree
Biblical name: none

Then he went away and hanged himself.
MATTHEW 27:5

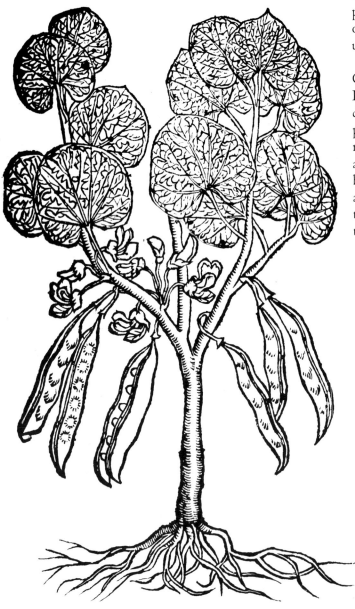

An ancient legend tells how the flowers of the tree from which Judas hanged himself, because he betrayed Jesus, turned bright pink for shame. *Cercis siliquastrum*, the Judas tree, produces flowers which are clustered together in bunches. They appear both on the new and on the older branches, and often even on the trunk, a rather rare phenomenon in trees. In southern Europe, where it is very common in the wild, *Cercis siliquastrum* grows to a height of 10m. As a rule it is rather smaller in cooler climates, but is still fairly resistant to frost. Younger specimens are more sensitive than the older, more well-developed trees. It is a good idea to cover the base of a young bush with a thick layer of fallen leaves or straw every winter to protect it.

The Judas tree is a fast-growing shrub with reddish-brown young shoots. The leaves are kidney-shaped and have seven clearly-defined veins. The small flowers appear before the leaves unfurl, and are clearly visible because of the absence of leaves. After pollination, many pod-shaped fruits develop, which often remain hanging from the branches and trunk until far into the winter.

GROWING TIPS

In order to develop well, the Judas tree needs a great deal of sun. It does not make many demands on the soil, provided that it is well drained. It is particularly recommended for training against a wall. Plant it against a south-facing wall, and train the young branches in a regular pattern. It will have a striking appearance, particularly when it is flowering. It is easy to propagate the Judas tree, either from seed or by taking cuttings.

Crown Daisy

Scientific name: Chrysanthemum coronarium L.
Family name: Compositae
Natural habitat: Mediterranean area
English name: crown daisy
Biblical name: flower

All men are like grass, and all their glory is like the flowers of the field; the grass withers and the flowers fall ...
I PETER 1:24

The fields of the Mediterranean countries are full of brightly coloured flowers in the early spring. It is by no means inconceivable that the text quoted here and that in Isaiah 40:6 refer to this display. These flowers include many species from the family Compositae, of which the yellow flowering crown daisy, *Chrysanthemum coronarium*, and *Chrysanthemum segetum*, the corn marigold, which is also yellow in colour, usually predominate. These annuals, which readily seed themselves, flower from March onwards. Often all their splendour has disappeared by the beginning of May, or even earlier, because the sun has become so strong that it has shrivelled up the vegetation.

GROWING TIPS

Apart from the species which grow wild, there is a whole range of cultivated varieties with striking fancy names. You can buy the seeds at a seed merchant. Sow them in a sunny spot in spring, and the first plants will flower profusely after only 6–8 weeks. Any soil is suitable for this easy-to-grow plant. In addition to being beautiful as garden plants, these chrysanthemums are also suitable as cut flowers which last a long time.

CHRYSANTHEMUM CORONARIUM

Chickpea

Scientific name: Cicer arietinum
Family name: Leguminosae
Natural habitat: northern Africa, Ethiopia, the
     Mediterranean area, central Asia
English name: chickpea or garbanzo bean
Biblical name: vegetables

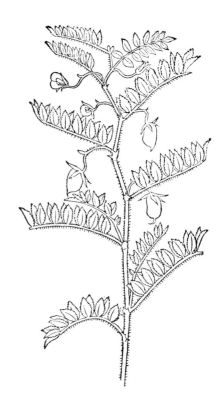

Please test your servants for ten days. Give us nothing but vegetables to eat and water to drink. Then compare our appearance with that of the young men who eat the royal food, and treat your servants in accordance with what you see.

DANIEL 1:12–13

The words 'food' and 'vegetables' refer in the Bible, among other things, to the dried seeds of broad beans (*Vicia faba*) and chickpeas (*Cicer arietinum*). The broad bean is well known as a vegetable, and is mostly eaten while it is fresh and green. The chick pea or garbanzo bean is less well known, and then mainly in its dried form.

Like most pea or bean plants, it belongs to the family of the Leguminosae. The genus *Cicer*, which comprises about twenty different species, is found growing wild in North Africa, Ethiopia, the Eastern Mediterranean and Central Asia. In these areas the chick pea is also cultivated on a large scale for its pea-

CICER ARIETINUM

sized seeds which are rich in starch. They are eaten baked and are also ground into flour, but they are consumed particularly in the way that we eat baked beans.

The species name, *arietinum*, from the Latin 'aries' (*arietis*, ram) is a reference to the seed's resemblance to the head of a ram. In 1644, the botanist Dodonaeus described the seeds of the chick pea in his book on herbs as follows: 'In our language these peas are generally known as angular or square peas, rather similar to the head of a lamb. These peas, that is, the angular ones referred to above, cause as much wind and flatulence when eaten as food as the faba bean (broad bean); but they feed the body better and more strongly. They encourage sleep, and it is commonly believed that they increase potency; and this is why some have given these peas to stallions to eat before they mount a mare.'

GROWING TIPS

It is almost impossible to grow chickpeas except in warm, subtropical regions, where the plants will reach maturity and produce ripe seeds in the constant sunshine. You will only succeed in harvesting fully-grown seeds in cooler climates after a very hot, dry summer. Even then the yield will not be large. The chickpea plant is a rather unattractive annual that can only be sown once the soil has been warmed up by the sun. As a rule this is not the case until the beginning of summer. The plant can grow to a height of 30–50cm and, in contrast with most other peas and beans, only produces one or two seeds per pod.

Wild Chicory

Scientific name: Cichorium intybus L.
Family name: Compositae
Natural habitat: southern Europe
English name: wild chicory
Biblical name: bitter herbs

. . . that same night they are to eat the meat roasted over the fire, along with bitter herbs, and bread made without yeast.

EXODUS 12:8

Although wild chicory is one of the best-known bitter herbs which grows in Mediterranean countries, the cultivated form *(Cichorium intybus)* was developed through a long process of selection. In the Netherlands, where the plant is found particularly along dikes and by rivers, it is a striking plant which flowers profusely in its second year.

Cichorium is the Latin version of the Greek word *kichorion*, chicory, while the name of the species is derived from the Latin word *intybum* or *intybus*, which means chicory or endive.

Originally, the leaves of the *Cichorium pumilum* were gathered, as well as the leaves of other species of *Cichorium*, to be eaten as a salad with other leaves of bitter tasting, herb-like plants. Endive *(Cichorium endivia)* is a green vegetable which is virtually indistinguishable from *Cichorium intybus* when it is flowering, and has the same bitter taste. Just as in Bible times, these plants are still gathered and eaten today by people who live in that area and who eat the leaves with lamb and unleavened bread.

During the first year after it is sown, this biennial develops a large tap root and a compact rosette of leaves. Modern cultivated varieties have roots which are used to grow the blanched chicons, and are harvested at the end of the first season in the autumn. Although the green leaves are suitable for consumption, they are rarely eaten here, because they are bitter and tough. However, when they are blanched, the bitter taste largely disappears and is replaced by a pleasant taste which is widely appreciated.

CICHORIUM
INTYBUS

Chicory is still a relatively recent vegetable. It was chance that led the gardener Brézier at the botanical gardens in Brussels to discover that, after being stored in a dark place for some time, the roots developed white leaves which were good to eat. After a great deal of cross-fertilization and selection, the varieties we know now were cultivated.

In addition to its delicate taste, this 'bitter herb' has very few calories (17 per 100 g, as compared with approximately 27 per 100 g for other vegetables), so that it is eminently suitable for diets. Apart from this, it is also rich in insulin and minerals such as calcium and phosphorus.

In the past it was believed that the bitter juices which flow abundantly when the plant is damaged had medicinal properties. They were thought to help against gastric complaints and disorders of the gall bladder, liver and spleen. The roots were roasted and processed to produce substitute coffee.

In spring, the tall stems, which can reach a height of up to 120cm and have virtually no leaves, shoot up from the tap roots, and beautiful clusters of blue flowers, 3–5cm across, develop on the stems. The flowers do not open until the evening, and are at their most beautiful early in the morning. By midday they will close again if the sun is shining.

GROWING TIPS

In order to develop thick roots in the autumn, sow the seeds in early summer where the seeds are to grow, in rows approximately 30 cm apart. If the plants are too close together when the seeds come up, they should be thinned out to approximately 12–14cm apart.

The thickness of the roots to be harvested in autumn depends on the type of soil. Preferably it should be fairly poor, for in fertile soil the plant will develop thick foliage at the expense of the root. It is certainly not necessary to manure the soil or to add extra nutrients in the form of artificial fertilizer.

Lift the plants with a fork in autumn and pull them out of the soil by hand. Then cut the leaves from the roots in such a way that the growing tip is not damaged. In other words, leave behind a collar of several centimetres of leaf.

As long as the roots remain in the soil, they are quite hardy, but once they have been lifted, they are susceptible to frost. When you have lifted the plants, you can start to force them. Nowadays there are varieties which can be forced without being covered, which is a boon for the amateur gardener. It is quite a specialized topic, and you should consult a book on vegetables for full details about the variety you are using.

CICHORIUM INTYBUS

Cinnamon

Scientific name: Cinnamomum zeylanicum Blume
Family name: Lauraceae
Natural habitat: Sri Lanka, India
English name: cinnamon
Biblical name: cinnamon

. . . nard and saffron, calamus and cinnamon, with every kind
of incense tree . . .
SONG OF SONGS 4:14

The cinnamon tree was not found in the Holy Land in Bible times. The sweet-smelling bark, which was a highly prized trade item, was brought from China to Judea by the Phoenicians and the Arabs in caravans travelling through Persia. The well-known cinnamon sticks come from *Cinnamomum zeylanicum,* which belongs to the laurel family *(Lauraceae)*. These cinnamon sticks are the thin inner bark of young *Cinnamomum* branches four or five years old, which have been carefully gathered and then dried. Apart from its culinary use, cinnamon is also used for perfuming oils.

Cinnamomum zeylanicum grows into an enormous tree. In tropical countries cinnamon trees are planted on a large scale on special plantations. Here they are usually grown as bushes, which makes the harvest easier. Indonesia is a particularly important producer. During the colonial era the Dutch laid the foundations for extensive cultivation of this spice.

GROWING TIPS

In cooler climates the different *Cinnamomum* varieties are easy to grow in tubs. Some specialist nurseries sell the young plants on a small scale. They can be placed outside in a warm, sunny spot from early summer to autumn. During the winter months they should be kept in a cool, frost-free place. The plant can be propagated by sowing seeds or by taking cuttings. The latter will take root with the help of growth hormones at a temperature of approximately 23–25°C, although this is not always an easy process.

CINNAMOMUM ZEYLANICUM

Rock Rose

Scientific name:	Cistus incanus (L.) ssp. creticus (L.) Heywood
Family name:	Cistaceae
Natural habitat:	Europe, Greece
English name:	rock rose
Biblical name:	myrrh

. . . they looked up and saw a caravan of Ishmaelites coming from Gilead. Their camels were loaded with spices, balm and myrrh, and they were on their way to take them down to Egypt.

GENESIS 37:25

All *Cistus* species—and there are about twenty different species plus an equal number of cultivated varieties—belong to the Cistaceae family. They have a preference for arid soil in the southern regions of Europe and are found as far away as Iran and the Canary Islands. They are a feature of the vegetation type known as the *maquis*, the thick impenetrable undergrowth of the dry coastal regions of the Mediterranean. The many species of rock rose, including *C. ladaniferus* and *C. albidus*, flower profusely in spring along with numerous other plants, making the *maquis* particularly beautiful.

The leaves and young shoots contain many essential oils, and when you walk among these plants, they release a pleasant smell, as well as secreting a sticky, resinous substance. This resin is collected during the heat of the day on a stick wound with soft cloths. In the past, goats which browsed on these plants were sometimes used as collectors: the resinous substance got stuck in the goats' beards, and in the evening the goatherds could scrape it off. They would knead it into balls and sell the resin under the name *laudanum*, also known as 'Arabic Ladan', which was written in the past as *Labdanum* and *Ladanum*. The name *laudanum* is derived from the Latin word *laudare* which means 'to praise'. This name used to be given to a number of praiseworthy medicines, and nowadays it is still used to indicate various opium preparations.

Laudanum is soft, dark brown or black in colour, and has a bitter taste. For a long time it was very commonly used in the preparation of a number of different medicines. Nowadays it is still used in the perfume industry, and occasionally also in the preparation of ointments or salves.

An extremely beautiful parasitical plant often grows in the roots of the rock rose. This is *Cytinus hypocistus*, which belongs to the Rafflesiaceae family. It is

fairly small, but you notice it immediately because of the brilliant bright orange colour of the flowers.

GROWING TIPS

Rock roses are not very hardy in the garden, with one exception: *Cistus laurifolius*, which can survive in cooler climates for a long time. In a sunny, sheltered spot, this evergreen shrub can reach a height of approximately 150cm.

In summer the branches are covered with small, snowy-white, yellow-hearted flowers, 5–7cm across. You can grow other species successfully in pots or tubs. Keep them in a light cool place that is frost-free throughout the winter.

CISTUS LADANIFER

CISTUS ALBIDUS

Bitter-apple

Scientific name: Citrullus colocynthis (L.) Schrader
Family name: Cucurbitaceae
Natural habitat: the Mediterranean area, northern
    Africa, southern Asia
English name: bitter-apple
Biblical name: gourds

---

*. . . and found a wild vine. He gathered some of its gourds and
filled the fold of his cloak.*
2 KINGS 4:39

A traditional proverb speaks of things that are 'as bitter
as gall'. Anyone who has ever tasted the fruit of the
bitter-apple *(Citrullus colocynthis)* will never forget the
meaning of the word 'bitter'. This bitter melon is
indigenous to the arid regions of the Mediterranean. It
is a perennial which completely dies off during the dry
season, except for the fleshy root which remains
behind. Only the fruits, which often remain dried out
in the sand, are left to mark the place where the plant

once grew. Well-developed plants produce a number of
long runners covered in coarse hair, and fruits the size
of a large orange. Before they are quite ripe, the fruits
are dappled light and dark green, while the flesh of the
fruit is white and contains a large number of small
brown seeds.

    The fruits are not suitable for consumption, but
they have been traditionally used as an efficient, though
by no means safe, laxative. In addition, the plants are
occasionally grown by enthusiasts for the beautifully
patterned fruits which keep for a long time and can be
very decorative, as can other gourds.

GROWING TIPS
Where the climate is significantly cooler than that of
the Holy Land it is too cold to cultivate the bitter-
apple–at least outside. To grow the plant you will need
a cold frame or greenhouse where plants grown from
seed can be planted out approximately 75–100cm
apart. If they are to develop well, it is essential that the
soil is richly manured. They will usually grow well in
the high temperatures of the greenhouse caused by the
sun's rays, provided that you spray them every day with
cold water to prevent infestations of spiders, making
sure that you also spray the undersides of the leaves. In
addition, it is important to feed them with sufficient
nutrients.

Watermelon

Scientific name: Citrullus lanatus (Thunb.) Mansfeld.
Family name: Cucurbitaceae
Natural habitat: southern Europe and southern Africa
English name: watermelon
Biblical name: melon

We remember the fish we ate in Egypt at no cost—also the cucumbers, melons, leeks, onions and garlic.

NUMBERS 11:5

It is probably this melon which the people of Israel were thinking of when they were suffering the deprivations of the journey through the desert.

The Egyptians had grown *Citrullus lanatus* and *Cucumis melo* (the melon) for a long time, and they had already cultivated many large varieties by a process of selection. Today there are several cultivated varieties, with green or marbled, smooth and fairly hard, shiny skin. The sweet flesh of the fruit can be either dark red or light yellow, containing large numbers of small, shiny black seeds. Both genera belong to the cucumber family (Cucurbitaceae).

Another member of the cucumber family which was also indigenous to Egypt and can even sometimes be found growing wild in cooler countries is the squirting cucumber *(Ecballium elaterium)*, which is described in detail under its scientific name later on in this book.

GROWING TIPS

To grow watermelons successfully, you need a great deal of heat. In cooler climates you can only raise them in a cold frame or greenhouse. A wide choice of cultivated varieties is available from a well-stocked seed merchant. For further information about their cultivation, refer to *Citrullus colocynthis,* as well as following the instructions on the seed packet.

CITRULLUS
LANATUS

Blessed Thistle

Scientific name: Cnicus benedictus L.
Family name: Compositae
Natural habitat: Mediterranean area, central and
                     southeastern Europe
English name: blessed thistle
Biblical name: thistle

*By their fruit you will recognise them. Do people pick grapes
from thornbushes, or figs from thistles?*
MATTHEW 7:16

CNICUS BENEDICTUS

Plants have to protect themselves against animals looking for food, particularly in arid regions. One of the ways in which they can repel animals is to arm themselves with thorns, and this is the reason why there are so many plants in the Middle East with small or large thorns. One of the many thistles found in the Holy Land is the blessed thistle, *Cnicus benedictus*, which is relatively lightly armed with thorns. The popular name of this plant is derived from the Latin name for the species *benedictus*, which means 'blessed'.

This thistle has a famous place in the history of Scotland. During the Danish wars the Danes wished to mount a surprise attack on the Scots at night. In order to make as little noise as possible, the Danes moved about in their bare feet. However, when one of the soldiers stepped on a thistle by accident and cried out in pain, the Scots were warned and were able to repel the attack. Since that time the 'guardian thistle' has been the symbol of Scotland. The emblem is accompanied by the appropriate motto: *'Nemo me impugne lacessit'*.

GROWING TIPS

Seeds of the annual plant, *Cnicus benedictus*, which belongs to the family Compositae, are available from seed merchants. Sow them in a sunny spot in spring. The plant tolerates almost any type of soil. When it is fully grown, it will reach a height of approximately 60cm, so it will sometimes be necessary to stake it.

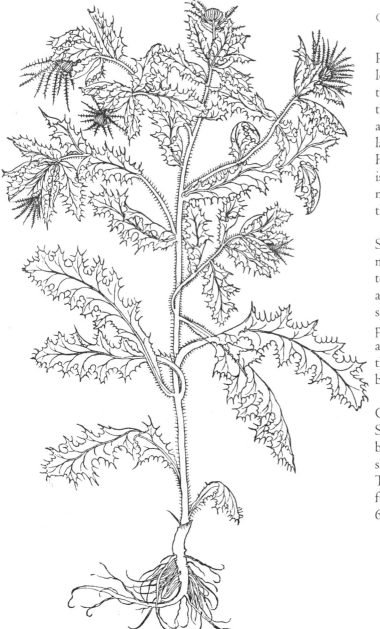

Myrrh

Scientific name: Commiphora myrrha (Nees) Engler
Family name: Burseraceae
Natural habitat: Arabia
English name: myrrh
Biblical name: myrrh

On coming to the house, they saw the child with his mother Mary, and they bowed down and worshipped him. Then they opened their treasures and presented him with gifts of gold and of incense and of myrrh.

MATTHEW 2:11

The genus *Commiphora*, which comprises approximately 135 different species and forms part of the *Burseraceae* family, is found in an area which extends across the hot countries of Africa, Madagascar, Arabia and West India, where it grows mainly in very arid regions. Some species produce the resin from which myrrh is made.

The fully grown plants can grow into sizeable bushes or small trees. The branches are thorny and covered with small leathery leaves through which very little moisture evaporates. The trunk is thick and in some species the bark is strikingly smooth and green in colour, indicating that, particularly during the dry season when the tree has no leaves, the process of photosynthesis takes place in the trunk. In order to obtain the resin, a cut is made in the main trunk. The sap that is caught has a clear, oily consistency and is white or yellowish in colour. It soon sets to a resin. In the Middle East this resin is still highly valued for its aromatic properties, and is used in the preparation of perfumes and medicines. In ancient Egypt the resin was burned in temples as incense, and it was also used for embalming the dead.

However, some experts consider that myrrh is a mixture of the resin from *Commiphora, Cistus,* and *Commiphora opobalsanum.* The latter grows in the natural state in south-west Arabia and Somalia. This resin is still used today in Catholic services.

GROWING TIPS

In our climate it is only possible to grow the various species of *Commiphora* in a greenhouse. The seed germinates very slowly at a temperature of 20–23° C The plant also grows extremely slowly and it takes quite a few years before it grows to any size at all. Bearing in mind the conditions of its natural habitat, *Commiphora* should be very sparingly watered, and then only during the period of growth between summer and early autumn. A myrrh plant will develop most successfully in well-drained soil composed of equal parts of peat and potting compost. It should not be given any manure, as this will cause it to produce long shoots. The most suitable place for cultivating *Commiphora* is a sunny greenhouse for succulents, where the temperature never falls below 5° C during the winter months.

COMMIPHORA MYRRHA

Coriander

Scientific name: Coriandrum sativum L.
Family name: Umbelliferae
Natural habitat: southern Europe, northern Africa, western Asia
English name: coriander
Biblical name: coriander (seed)

The people of Israel called the bread manna. It was white like coriander seed and tasted like wafers made with honey.
EXODUS 16:31

Coriander, *Coriandrum sativum*, is an annual plant which grows to a height of 40–70cm It belongs to the family Umbelliferae and is an indigenous plant in Southwest Asia. The name *Coriandrum* is believed to derive from the Greek word *koris*, which means insect. This is a clear reference to the smell that it gives off when it is so much as touched, which is similar to the smell produced by some insects. The spherical fruits, about the size of peppercorns, which are known as coriander seed, are used for all sorts of purposes. Coriander was used as a culinary spice and as a medicine long before the birth of Christ, as shown by the above text. Today, finely ground coriander seed is used in the preparation of the Dutch delicacy *muisjes*, eaten on bread. Coriander seed is also used for preserving fruit and gherkins, in herbal vinegar and in the preparation of several different liqueurs. It is used in Indonesian cooking, where it is known as *ketumbar*. Finally, it is an important ingredient in curry powder, which is made from many different herbs and spices.

GROWING TIPS
It is not very difficult to grow coriander from seed, and takes only three months to be ready for harvesting. This means that the sowing period extends over a long time, from spring to late summer, so that the last plant to be grown can be harvested at the end of autumn. As coriander grows tap roots, it cannot easily be transplanted, so it must be sown *in situ*. If necessary, the plants can be thinned out later to prevent them from being overcrowded, which would stunt their growth. When the fruit is really ripe, the leaves gradually start to turn brown and eventually the plant dies off altogether. This is the time to harvest the plants. Pull them out of the soil by the roots, then tie them up in bunches and hang them up to dry upside-down in a well-ventilated, shaded place. After a few weeks, when the plants have thoroughly dried out, the spherical fruits can be threshed, or for smaller quantities, picked separately. Store in a dry place.

Saffron

Scientific name: Crocus sativus L.
Family name: Iridaceae
Natural habitat: southern and western Europe
English name: saffron
Biblical name: saffron

Your plants are an orchard of pomegranates, with choice fruits,
with henna and nard, nard and saffron, calamus and
cinnamon, with every kind of incense tree, with myrrh and aloes
and all the finest spices.
SONG OF SONGS 4:13–14

Saffron is the product of a number of different varieties of crocus, in particular *Crocus sativus*, which flowers with blue blooms in the autumn, unlike the more familiar spring crocuses . It is probably indigenous to Greece and Asia Minor, and belongs to the iris family (Iridaceae). Every year new bulbs are formed at the base of the old bulbs of the previous year. In order to prevent them from growing too far up in the course of the years, every bulb has ingenious roots with transverse wrinkles which pull the bulb down a little every year to keep it at the right depth. These so-called 'contractile roots' are clearly visible if a crocus is dug up while it is flowering.

The pistils, which have three styles, are collected for saffron and slowly dried over a charcoal fire or in the sun. No fewer than 150,000 to 250,000 of these styles are required to produce 1 kg of dried saffron. As *Crocus sativus* is sterile, producing no seed, it can only be propagated in a vegetative way: by means of the daughter corms, which are produced by the old bulbs. Because of the relatively low yield—approximately 20 kg of saffron is harvested per hectare per year—and the labour-intensive nature of the harvest, it is an extremely expensive product.

Saffron has also been cultivated in other countries. Nowadays, Spain, France, Italy, Austria and Switzerland have become the most important exporting countries. In the first half of this century Spain alone produced no less than 50,000 kg per year.

In ancient Egypt, saffron was used for the preparation of medicines and for spicing food. In addition, it was used for dyeing costly garments. Nowadays, saffron is used particularly to flavour food and drink and to colour it yellow. It gives dishes a characteristic sweet but, at the same time, slightly bitter taste. The quality of the dye is so strong that one part of saffron is enough to colour 200,000 parts of water.

Dried saffron is sold as threads, usually about 4–5cm long. Alternatively, it may be ground to a powder. The price is high, but very little is needed at a time. For example, for a large panful of rice, you only need one or one and a half 'threads' of saffron. When you are buying saffron, make sure that it is the genuine article that is for sale. The dried petals of the marigold, as well as the safflower, are well-known substitutes. For this reason it is better to buy the whole styles than the ground product in powder form.

GROWING TIPS

As noted above, *Crocus sativus* does not form any seed and is propagated vegetatively through the daughter corms which develop at the base of the old corm. Although it is not mass-produced, the saffron crocus is also sold by a few specialist bulb growers in the Netherlands.

The flowers appear in the autumn and are only produced by fully grown corms which are at least 1–1.5cm across. If they are to flower again the following year, they will need a nutritious, well-drained soil; it is essential to feed them with artificial fertilizer about six weeks after they have been planted out, and in the spring.

Much larger *Crocus sativus* corms are imported from India (Kashmir). These usually flower much more easily. They are sold under the name *Crocus sativus var. cashmirianus*, but are otherwise identical to the normal variety.

CROCUS SATIVUS

CROCUS SATIVUS

Cucumber/Gherkin

Scientific name:	Cucumis sativus L.
Family name:	Cucurbitaceae
Natural habitat:	southern Europe and India
English name:	cucumber/gherkin
Biblical name:	cucumber

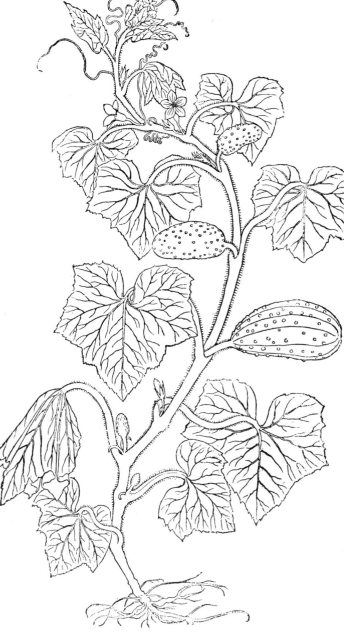

We remember the fish we ate in Egypt at no cost—also the cucumbers, melons, leeks, onions and garlic.

NUMBERS 11:5

The ancient Egyptians could no more have conceived of life without cucumbers and gherkins than can the Egyptians of today. These two crops are both varieties of *Cucumis sativus*, which belong to the Cucurbitaceae family. It is such a well-known food crop that it hardly needs any description. People have cultivated this vegetable, which is 99 per cent water, since the dawn of civilization. Although it is not possible to ascertain where exactly it originated, it is likely to have come from Southern Asia, and probably from India. Over the course of the centuries many varieties have been cultivated. Today you can find strains for all climates. They will all produce sizeable fruits, provided there is enough moisture in the soil.

GROWING TIPS

There are varieties which you can grow in the greenhouse, as well as others which you can grow outside. Some have green fruit; there are also some which produce white or yellow fruit. It is important to start the young plants early in the year if they are to be grown outside. They can be planted out from early summer onwards, which means that the seeds should be sown indoors a month earlier. If the crop is to succeed, you must manure the soil well. The weak trailing shoots can be trained up supports or left to grow over the ground. If they are not trained, place a glass plate underneath the fruit to prevent it from rotting.

CUCUMIS SATIVUS

Cumin

Scientific name: Cuminum cyminum L.
Family name: Umbelliferae
Natural habitat: Mediterranean area, northern Africa and southwest Europe
English name: cumin
Biblical name: cumin

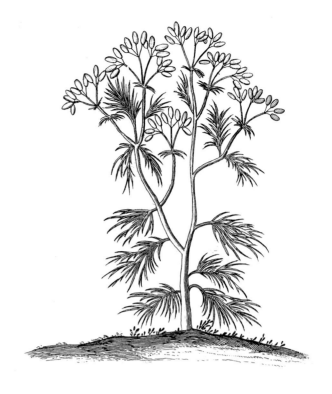

When he has levelled the surface, does he not sow caraway and scatter cumin?

ISAIAH 28:25

Some plants are so clearly identified in the Bible that there is absolutely no doubt as regards either the genus or the species. This certainly applies to *Cuminum cyminum*, a very common annual herb which belongs to the Umbelliferae family. It originated in Turkestan, and has been cultivated on a large scale since time immemorial. An accurate and detailed description of the harvest and the use of this plant is given in Isaiah 28:25–29.

Cumin is an annual plant which grows to a height of 15–50cm with long trifoliate leaves. The numerous white or pinkish flowers form broad umbels. The fruits, which vary in length from 5–10mm are prickly and are known as cumin seed. They are very similar to caraway seed, but are smaller and have a sharper taste. They are used, amongst other things, in some cheeses and for pickling cucumbers and gherkins. Cumin is also often used to flavour various dishes, including fish. In Germany in particular, it is sprinkled over bread before the bread goes into the oven.

GROWING TIPS
Cumin is a common kitchen herb and the seeds are easy to obtain. Sow the seeds outside in late spring and thin out the plants later if necessary. It is difficult to transplant them because of the well-developed tap root. The plant will thrive in any soil, provided it is not too wet. However, it does like to grow in the sun.

Cypress

Scientific name: Cupressus sempervirens
Family name: Cupressaceae
Natural habitat: southern Europe
English name: cypress
Biblical name: cypress

I will put in the desert the cedar and the acacia, the myrtle and the olive. I will set pines in the wasteland, the fir and the cypress together . . .

ISAIAH 41:19

Everybody is familiar with the pillar-like cypress. It was originally indigenous to the countries around the Mediterranean, and is now found in temperate countries all over the world, where it is planted next to churches and in cemeteries. It is precisely because of its striking form that the *Cupressus sempervirens* 'Stricta' with which we are concerned here is often planted in large and small gardens.

The original tree, *Cupressus sempervirens*, grew to enormous proportions. Since ancient times, there have been several varieties of this species, only one of which grows as mentioned above, like a pillar. The 'Horizontalis' variety is certainly no less striking, with its broad outward-growing branches. In addition to 15–20 genuine species of *Cupressus*, scores of cultivated varieties have also been developed in the course of the centuries. All these species and varieties are evergreen conifers.

When the fruit sets in *Cupressus sempervirens*, spherical green balls 2–3cm across develop. When these are ripe and slowly begin to turn brown, the 8–14 scales of the fruit burst open and the large, angular flat seeds are released. The balls themselves often remain on the branches for decades, sometimes becoming completely overgrown by the bark.

Apart from its well-known natural habitat in Mediterranean countries, various species of cypress are also found growing naturally in Asia and North America. The trees also survive very well in dry countries such as Israel because they have small, flattened scales or needles which are pressed against the branches so that very little moisture evaporates. In these regions growth is minimal, producing a very hard and durable timber which contains a lot of resin and therefore lasts for centuries. A great deal of cypress wood was used in the construction of King Solomon's temple, in addition to the famous cedarwood. Even earlier, the ancient Egyptians used the wood to make sarcophagi, and in Greece it is still used for this purpose. The huge church doors of St Peter's in Rome are also made of cypress wood, and after many centuries they still show no signs of decay.

GROWING TIPS

Cupressus seeds will soon germinate if you sow them in the spring in a pot of garden soil or moist peat, place them in the windowsill and water them well. When they have been repotted, the young, bluish-green seedlings can be planted out in individual pots in early summer and dug into the garden in a sunny spot. If you repot them once or twice more during the growing season, the young cypress trees will have grown to a height of more than 50cm by the autumn. Bring them inside by the end of autumn and keep them in a frost-free place for the winter. Because of the low temperature, they will hardly grow during this season, so they do not need any water. Repot the plants again in early summer, and put them back out in the garden.

Few people know that despite its natural habitat in hot climates, the cypress can withstand quite a bit of frost. A two-year old specimen planted outside in a warm, sunny and sheltered spot will soon strongly develop into a slender tree which will survive winter temperatures of ¯10–¯15° C reasonably well, provided the base of the tree is covered with a mulch such as peat. Usually it is cold weather and freezing winds which cause branches to freeze; this becomes clear in the late spring when the branches completely discolour and turn brown. When this happens, remove the dead wood, and the remaining branches will usually grow out.

Most cypresses do very well as indoor conifers. Species which are specially cultivated for this purpose include the pillar-shaped *Cupressus macrocarpa* 'Goldcrest', which is slightly more sensitive to frost and has a beautiful yellow colour, and *Cupressus cashmeriana*, which is even more frost-sensitive. It has elegant, steel-blue hanging branches. Indoors, cypresses prefer a light spot which is slightly chilly to a dark place which is too warm. If it is too warm, the plant will inevitably be attacked by red spider mite, and if there is too little light, the plant will soon outgrow its strength and become tall, weak and unsightly.

Cyclamen

Scientific name: Cyclamen persicum Miller
Family name: Primulaceae
Natural habitat: Europe, the Mediterranean area to Iran
English name: cyclamen
Biblical name: lily

I am a rose of Sharon, a lily of the valleys.
Like a lily among thorns is my darling among the maidens.
SONG OF SONGS 2:1–2

At the time that the Bible was written, no one would have thought that the beautifully flowering cyclamen would ever become one of the most popular house plants. It is now such a well-known and common pot plant that there cannot be anyone who is not familiar with it. It belongs to the primula family (Primulaceae). The present large-scale cultivation of the cyclamen with large flowers was preceded by a great deal of selection by

division. The original variety of *Cyclamen persicum*, which can be found in many Mediterranean countries, flowers in spring with just a few or several pale pink flowers, depending on its position. If the soil is very stony, the large rootstocks grow almost at the surface. They can be found in the strangest places: under deciduous or coniferous trees, growing in loose earth, rich in humus; in cracks in rocks, between stones and dry stone walls; in the hollows in trees, and other unusual places where the rootstocks seem to be falling out because they have developed to such a large size over the years.

The name of the genus *Cyclamen* is derived from the ancient Greek plant name *Kuklamtnon* or *Kuklamtnos*, based on the Greek word *kuklos* or *kyklos*, meaning a circle or round disk. The description refers to the circular shape of the tubers. In former times the tubers, and particularly the juices from them, were used in folk medicine.

GROWING TIPS

The so-called wild species of cyclamen can broadly be divided into two groups: spring flowering and autumn flowering. The species which flower in the Mediterranean spring include *Cyclamen coum* (December to May), *C. persicum* (February to April), *C. pseud. ibericum* (January to March) and *C. repandum* (March to May). Those which flower in the autumn include *C. cilicicum* (September to November), *C. hederifolium* (syn: *C. neapolitanum*) (July to November), and *C. purpurascens* (syn: *C. europaeum*) (June to October).

Most cyclamens need a Mediterranean climate to flourish, as is to be expected in view of their natural habitat. This means hot, dry summers, rain during the spring and autumn, and low temperatures in the winter. The period of frost may therefore not be too long. Only very few varieties can be cultivated successfully outside throughout the year in cooler climates, where frost sometimes lasts for a long time in winter. Varieties which can tolerate this include *C. coum*, *purpurascens*, *hederifolium* and *cilicicum*. The following varieties are more sensitive to frost: *C. mirabile, pseud. ibericum, parviflorum* and *repandum*.

Other varieties must be cultivated where they are not exposed to frost: in pots, or in the ground of a cold greenhouse, and treated as for alpine plants.

For successful results it is advisable not to use imported tubers. Despite the fact that these are very attractive because they are often enormous in size, and appear to promise prolific flowering, it is generally a very long time before they really start to grow. Sometimes they do not even grow at all because the tubers rot away before then.

Furthermore, all varieties of cyclamens belong to a group of protected plants, and trading them is prohibited. Only a very small percentage may be officially imported every year. However, you can virtually be sure of success with tubers grown from seed. If the tubers are stored and sold in damp moss after they have been dug up, so that the roots do not get a chance to dry out, they will continue to grow quickly once they have been planted out. To ensure that they grow well, the soil should be airy, well-drained, and rich in humus, with good drainage. In addition, they thrive best in a slightly shady spot in the garden, for example, under bushes.

All varieties produce ripe seed in the middle of summer, regardless of when they flower, which varies greatly from variety to variety. The seed germinates at the same time as the leaves of the fully grown plant begin to show above the ground. Although the seeds can be sown in any type of soil, peat is particularly good. The seeds should be pressed down into the soil, covered and well watered.

To prevent the seeds from drying out, cover with a plate of glass and a layer of newspaper. As bought seed has always been dried, it is advisable to pre-soak the seeds for 24 hours before sowing, so that they will germinate more quickly.

Cyclamens which are cultivated as indoor plants do best in a light spot which is not too hot. In addition, it is essential to keep the soil in the pot moist at all times. When the plant is flowering, it is also a good idea to add some artificial fertilizer to the water with which the soil is watered. Excess water should be removed from the saucer after half an hour to prevent the roots from rotting, as cyclamens hate having 'wet feet'.

CYCLAMEN PERSICUM

Papyrus Reed

Scientific name: Cyperus papyrus L.
Family name: Cyperaceae
Natural habitat: central Africa, Nile Valley, Sicily
English name: papyrus reed
Biblical name: reeds

---

*But when she could hide him no longer, she got a papyrus basket
for him and coated it with tar and pitch. Then she placed the child
in it and put it among the reeds along the bank of the Nile.*

EXODUS 2:3–4

Cyperus papyrus is one of the best-known Bible plants. It
is immediately associated with the story of Moses in his
basket of reeds, and obviously also with the celebrated
papyrus scrolls.

CYPERUS PAPYRUS

Papyrus was made from the lower parts of the thick
triangular stems of papyrus reed, which can grow more
than 3m tall. It was fairly simple to prepare. The pieces
of the stem were first peeled off, and then cut up into
long, thin slices which were arranged in layers at right
angles to each other. Additional layers produced a
stronger quality. The resulting sheet was beaten with
pumice stone so that the juices of the plant, which are
sticky, acted as an adhesive. When the papyrus sheet
had been dried, it could be cut to the required size.

Because of the light structure of the stems, the
Egyptians also used the reed to build small boats which
floated well and were used by fishermen and others.
The stems were woven into mats, or used for making
shoes. The young shoots were eaten when they had just
started growing, while more mature reeds were used as
fuel instead of wood, which was very scarce in Egypt.

At the time of Moses the papyrus plant was still
very common along the banks of the Nile. Nowadays,
the plant's range is largely restricted to southern Nubia.
The rootstocks, which become entangled, form
enormous floating masses which are virtually
impenetrable. For this reason, waterways where
papyrus reeds grow profusely are extremely difficult to
penetrate because the navigable channels are constantly
changing. In severe winds and storms particularly, the
enormous floating islands move about quickly, often
breaking into smaller clumps which can block channels
completely.

GROWING TIPS

As *Cyperus papyrus* grows to such a size in its natural
habitat, you might think that it should be simple to
grow this plant at home without any problems.
Nothing could be further from the truth. In the first
place, the plant requires a great deal of light.
Furthermore, fairly high temperatures and a high
relative humidity are essential for cultivation to be
successful. The plants must be grown in a watertight
tank which should always be full. If all these conditions
are met, the papyrus reed will grow fairly well in the
living room or in the greenhouse.

The plants will even flourish outside in the garden
in a sheltered sunny spot during the summer months. In
winter the temperature should not fall below 15 °C, or
the thick rootstocks will rot in the cold. In contrast
with the umbrella plant, *Cyperus alternifolius,* which is far
more suitable for indoor cultivation, papyrus reed
cannot be propagated from leaf cuttings, but only by
dividing from the rootstocks or from seed.

Burning Bush

Scientific name:	Dictamnus albus L.
Family name:	Rutaceae
Natural habitat:	southern and central Europe to eastern Russia
English name:	burning bush
Biblical name:	bush

He saw that though the bush was on fire it did not burn up.
EXODUS 3:2

Translators of the Bible and botanists have sometimes made only superficial attempts to identify the plants referred to in the Bible. The reason for this is probably that they generally knew little or nothing of the flora in the Holy Land.

There were many explanations for the phenomenon of the 'burning bush' described in Exodus 3:2–4. At a time when the belief in miracles was waning, and 'scientific' explanations were sought to explain anything that was described in the Bible as a 'miracle', an ordinary botanical explanation was sought for the phenomenon. The acacia was considered a possibility, as it shoots up from the brushwood and can be covered with *Loranthus acaciae*, a semi-parasite related to mistletoe. When this semi-parasite is in bloom, the bright red colour of the many small flowers is very striking. From a distance it could give an impression of 'burning'. But later, Moses examines the plant more closely (Exodus 3:3), so an impression from afar would not be enough.

Others thought of *Dictamnus albus*, known as the 'burning bush'. This herbal plant, which can grow up to 1m tall, contains so many volatile oils that if there is any fire in the vicinity on a hot summer's day, the whole plant can suddenly ignite like a burning torch.

This plant is a small miracle in its own right. But exactly what Moses saw is beyond the scope of this book.

GROWING TIPS

Although it is easier to purchase *Dictamnus* plants directly from a garden centre, it is also possible to grow the plants from seed. Quite a lot of care is needed before the seed-raised plants will flower. If you sow the shiny black seeds outside in a seed tray or flowerpot in the late summer, they may germinate in the following spring but it is not unusual for germination to take another year.

Once the seedlings have grown large enough to be replanted, transfer them to individual pots. The development from seedling to flowering plant is rather slow; the first flowering spikes will only appear after two or three years.

To really come into their own, these plants need a warm and sunny spot in the garden. It is also important that the soil is rich in nutrients and well drained. The longer the plant is left in the same spot, the more intensely it will flower. Once a strong specimen has developed, it would be interesting to try and see whether it will actually ignite if you place a lighted match near it on a hot summer's evening—whether it really deserves the name 'burning bush'.

DICTAMNUS ALBUS

Squirting Cucumber

Scientific name:	Ecballium elaterium (L.) A. Richard
Family name:	Cucurbitaceae
Natural habitat:	southern Europe
English name:	gourd
Biblical name:	gourd

... and found a wild vine. He gathered some of its gourds and filled the fold of his cloak.

2 KINGS 4:39

The gourd referred to in 2 Kings 4:39 might have been one of a number of plants, but the most probable would seem to be *Citrullus colocynthis* and *Ecballium elaterium*, which grow wild in the same natural habitat, and both produce very bitter fruit.

One of the characteristics of the bitter-apple is that the round fruit is easy to gather, but the squirting cucumber breaks open with such force that little or nothing of the fruit as such remains. It is by no means unlikely that the poison mentioned in Jeremiah 8:14, 9:15, and 23:15 was prepared from the fruits of both these plants.

ECBALLIUM ELATERIUM

GROWING TIPS

The fact that this gourd is sometimes found growing wild in cooler climates is proof that there are no problems in cultivating it. Sow the seeds, which are only sold by specialist seed merchants, directly into the soil in a warm spot in the garden at the end of spring. They will germinate quickly, particularly when the temperature rises. The plant, which does not grow much taller than 20–25cm in poor soil, has bluish green heart-shaped leaves covered with bristly hairs. In more nutritious soil the growth will be correspondingly more prolific. The yellow flowers produce a large, bristly, elliptical fruit which separates from the stem when it is ripe, and the contents squirt out of this opening.

Wild Olive

Scientific name: Elaeagnus angustifolia L.
Family name: Elaeagnaceae
Natural habitat: southern Europe, subtropical Asia
English name: wild olive
Biblical name: olive

I will put in the desert the cedar and the acacia, the myrtle and the olive.

ISAIAH 41:19

The wild olive, which was originally indigenous to the countries of the Mediterranean, and is also found as far away as central Asia, is also fairly common further north. The scholar Carolus Clusius first grew it, in the botanical gardens in Leiden, Holland in 1594.

Elaeagnus angustifolia, the scientific name of the wild olive or oleaster, belongs to the Elaeagnaceae family, and is therefore not related to the true olive, which comes from the family Oleaceae. About forty-five different species of *Elaeagnus* are known, found in North America as well as in the areas mentioned above. The species with which we are concerned here lives up to its name. *Angustifolia* is based on two Latin words—*angustus,* meaning 'narrow', and *folium* meaning 'leaf', and it certainly has narrower leaves than other wild olives.

As the tree grows in dry places with little rainfall, it protects itself against too much evaporation by a rather thick layer of silvery scales on each leaf, which are closer together at the bottom of the leaf than at the top. The stems of the young shoots also have scales. The younger branches, which sometimes die off through lack of water, act as thorns, so that the wild olive can look very prickly. The young one-year-old shoots produce large numbers of wonderfully fragrant, creamy-white flowers in May or June. After fertilization, the ovary slowly starts to develop into a fruit which looks exactly like an olive, except that it has a silvery colour because of the many small scales. The side which is exposed to the sun turns an orange or reddish colour. The Dutch name of 'olive willow' is therefore very suitable for its willow-like leaves and olive-like fruit.

The core of the fruit is a long stone with many long grooves, surrounded by a thick layer of floury flesh which is edible, but usually has a rather bitter taste. Nomads dry this fruit, grind it and then use it for baking bread.

The wild olive looks rather like an olive tree from a distance, hence its name. However, although oil can be produced from the fruit, it is suitable only for medicinal purposes.

The wood is particularly hard and durable. The heart of the wood is a beautiful dark-brown colour, while the sapwood is a creamy white. It is especially suitable for wood carving.

GROWING TIPS

As remarked earlier, the wild olive thrives in cooler climates. It grows very quickly, and after approximately fifteen years will grow into a small tree, slightly taller than 6m. Because of their superficial root systems, the fully-grown trees are vulnerable to strong winds, and it is not unusual for them to be blown over. Nevertheless, they form ideal vegetation for coastal areas because they are resistant to salt-laden breezes, on account of the protective layers of scales on the leaves, young stems and fruit.

E. angustifolia is fairly easy to grow from seed, and will thrive in any soil, including heavy clay. There are quite a number of different varieties, each with a characteristic leaf shape.

ELAEAGNUS ANGUSTIFOLIA

Rocket

Scientific name:	Eruca vesicaria (L.) (av.) ssp. sativa (Miller) Thell.
Family name:	Cruciferae
Natural habitat:	Mediterranean area, northern Africa, Israel
English name:	rocket
Biblical name:	herbs

One of them went out into the fields to gather herbs . . .
2 KINGS 4:39

In the original Hebrew Bible, the word 'oroth' is used for 'herbs', while in the Talmud, the Jewish commentary on the Old Testament, the word 'gargir' is used. The original inhabitants of the Middle East, including the Bedouins, collected a number of wild herbs as vegetables and then cooked them to a mush. One of the best known of these herbs, which is known in Arabic as 'jarjir', has the generic name *Eruca* and belongs to the Cruciferae family.

Eruca vesicaria subsp. *sativa* (syn: *Eruca sativa*) is known as rocket in English. It is very common in the countries of the Mediterranean and is by no means unknown in Israel, particularly in poor regions. It is actually a field weed, but is used as a vegetable. In addition, oil is pressed from the seeds as it is from black mustard (*Brassica nigra*) and rape seed (*Brassica napus*).

Rocket is an annual which can grow up to a height of about 1m, depending on the composition of the soil. Irregular leaves, often with deep indentations, develop on the stems. Rather large, creamy-white flowers appear, consisting of four petals each marked with a mauve vein. When they have been pollinated, the rocket-like fruits develop, containing smooth, round, brown seeds.

Eruca is a very old Latin name, and it is not possible to say where it originates. Some experts think it is related to the Greek word *ereugesthai,* which means to burp or belch. Others believe that the name is derived from the Latin word *urere,* which means to burn. In either case the name could be a reference to the sharpness of the plant, which can cause belching, especially when it is eaten raw. However, it is precisely because of its spicy taste that many people value it as a vegetable.

The seeds have as sharp a taste as the leaves, and are often used to replace peppercorns. A gram of seed will contain 550 grains. It is very light and rich in oil, so it can germinate up to about four years after being harvested.

GROWING TIPS
Rocket has become increasingly popular as a vegetable, particularly for adding to salads. As it is not sold for this purpose, however, enthusiasts will have to grow the plant in their own gardens.

It is no trouble to grow. The seeds can be sown in the open ground in early spring. Make sure that the soil is always moist, and the plants will grow rapidly. If it is wet enough, the leaves are tender and the sharp taste is slightly reduced. The leaves can be harvested after six to eight weeks. If you wish to have a supply of fresh leaves for a long period, it is advisable to sow at regular intervals throughout the season. The first sowing can then be kept for seed production.

ERUCA VESICARIA SSP. SATIVA

Ferula

Scientific name: Ferula galbaniflua Boiss. et Buhse
Family name: Umbelliferae
Natural habitat: Iran
English name: ferula
Biblical name: galbanum

Then the Lord said to Moses, 'Take fragrant spices—gum resin, onycha, and galbanum . . .'
EXODUS 30:34

Some species of the *Ferula* genus, in the Umbelliferae family, produce a substance called galbanum. It is a gum resin extracted from the lower parts of the stem and the thick base of the leaves of the plant. When these are cut, the sap that is released dries to form amber-coloured resinous drops which were once as valuable as gold.

There are approximately 135 known species of *Ferula,* most of which are found in the countries of the Mediterranean and in western and central Asia. In regions where *Ferula communis* grows prolifically, such as Greece, Crete, and above all, Cyprus, the plant is immediately noticeable because of the enormous branched stalks which grow to a height of 3–4m and are covered with umbels consisting of numerous small yellow flowers.

The name *Ferula* is a very old Latin plant name given by Linneaus to a plant with extremely tall stems, which were sometimes used as splints for broken limbs. The flower stems were also sturdy, and used in ancient times as a cane for naughty schoolchildren. According to some experts, the name is derived from the Latin *ferire,* which means 'to beat', and refers to the use of these stalks for corporal punishment—a *ferula* was a cane. Others prefer to think the name is derived from *ferre* in the sense of rising up; this refers to the great height to which the plant grows.

A striking feature of this giant fennel, as the plant is also known, is that it will flower profusely one year, while in the next year there will be virtually no specimen to be found in the same area. The reason for this is that the plant requires so much energy to flower, that it takes several years to regain its strength. This is in contrast to the species of a more modest size, which can flower every year, such as, for example, *Ferula assa-foetida.* The roots of this plant, which is particularly common in Iran, produce asafoetida, which is used as a spice in dishes and for medicinal purposes.

GROWING TIPS

Only a small number of *Ferula* species are hardy in cooler climates. One of these is the beautiful *Ferula assa-foetida,* a perennial plant which will grow to a height of approximately 2m and is extremely decorative in the garden when it is flowering, despite the unpleasant smell of the foliage. Although it can be propagated by division, it is easily grown from seed.

The most suitable time for sowing the seed is late summer. Transplant the young seedlings, and when they have grown sufficiently, plant them in nursery beds or in separate pots, so that they can be set out in their permanent place in the spring. They will need a sunny spot and a fairly rich, well-drained soil. During the winter the plants should be covered over, so that the roots do not freeze. The cut flowers, which have abundant yellowish-green umbels, are ideal for use in bouquets of mixed flowers.

▲▼ FERULA COMMUNIS

Fig

Scientific name: Ficus carica L.
Family name: Moraceae
Natural habitat: southern Europe
English name: fig
Biblical name: fig

When the woman saw that the fruit of the tree was good for food and pleasing to the eye, and also desirable for gaining wisdom, she took some and ate it. She also gave some to her husband, who was with her, and he ate it. Then the eyes of both of them were opened, and they realized that they were naked; so they sowed fig leaves together and made coverings for themselves.

GENESIS 3:6–7

In this story of the Fall, the fruit referred to is not an apple, but the fig leaves certainly refer to the leaves of the *Ficus carica*. In any case, the fig tree came into use early on, and it is mentioned more than fifty times in the Bible by its common names. Apart from the olive, it was undoubtedly one of the most important trees of the time. Nowadays the fig tree is still important to the people of Mediterranean countries.

As a rule it grows like a woody bush, but sometimes it can grow into a characteristic tree approximately 10m tall. It is very common both growing naturally and as a cultivated tree.

Ficus carica was probably originally indigenous to South-west Asia. It was widely cultivated even in the time of the ancient Egyptians, mainly for its valuable fruit. Nowadays groves of fig trees can still be found on a large scale in those areas. In addition, the tree is found in large numbers in many gardens in the Middle East, where it can be either planted on its own or in groups.

Normally a fig tree bears fruit at least twice a year. The first figs, also known as winter figs, develop on the old wood and ripen in June. In general they are eaten fresh. The summer figs grow on the new branches and are harvested in August or September. When they have been thoroughly dried, they are kept for use in winter.

Figs also have a medicinal value. In the east they are used as a remedy for boils and other eruptions on the skin in the same way that the prophet Isaiah treated the disease of Hezekiah, as described in 2 Kings 20:7. The fruit of the fig tree was also known to act as an excellent laxative. According to Pliny, figs were the best food for people who were very weak after an illness.

In the past, when the self-fertilizing varieties had not yet been developed, a process called caprification was used to ensure that the fruit was good. Some fig trees only have so-called 'seed figs', which means that they have only female flowers, while others produce not only male flowers, but also gall flowers (so-called caprificus). The inedible fruit of these gall flowers (caprifigs) harbour a species of wasp belonging to the genus *Blastophaga*, and these wasps were allowed to penetrate into the fruit of the edible variety from the inedible capri-figs, resulting in cross-fertilization and development of the fruit. Caprification was a process used as long ago as 4000 BC.

Although Judas was supposed to have hanged himself from a tree which owes its name to him, the Judas tree *(Cercis siliquastrum)*, there are other legends in which the tree concerned was a fig tree. It is precisely because the fig was so important at that time that there are many fascinating stories about it. The importance of the tree for the Israelites can be illustrated, for example, by the fact that when the ancient prophets berated believers for their weaknesses, they always threatened that the grape and fig harvest would be ruined. However, if they kept their promises, their crops would be preserved. Among the Jews, the phrase 'seated under one's vine or fig tree' was a reference to peace and prosperity.

There are at least as many non-biblical tales. An ancient story relates how Mary was seeking shelter for the infant Jesus when she was being pursued by Herod's soldiers, who wished to kill the child. The trunk of a fig tree opened up and she was able to hide inside it with her child until the soldiers had disappeared. Another legend tells how the fig was created by the Roman god of wine, Bacchus. According to this story there was a fig tree on the spot where Rome is now, and the crib containing Romulus and Remus became entangled in its branches while floating down the river Tiber. This was supposedly the reason why the ancient Romans worshipped the fig tree.

GROWING TIPS

Although the fig tree was originally a sub-tropical plant, it grows reasonably well in cooler climates. Obviously, a number of specific conditions must be met for the tree to develop well. It is very important to make sure that you plant it in an extremely warm and sheltered spot. A south-facing wall is ideal. Fill the hole in which the tree is to be planted with good soil, rich in nutrients, and the young fig tree will develop best.

The plant can usually be supplied by garden centres if it is ordered in advance. It often consists of only one shoot, and will grow fast in the first year. The best time to plant a fig tree is in early spring. However, pot-grown trees can also be planted out later in the season, even when the characteristic leaves have already formed. It is useful to tie back the young shoot regularly to supporting canes, thus preventing damage in strong winds.

The fig tree is sensitive to hard frost. It is best to take no risks and wrap the plant up from the beginning of December. The lower parts of the branches should be carefully protected in particular. Straw mats provide adequate protection for the higher branches. In general, a strong cold wind will do more damage than a severe frost and can cause freezing.

The protective wrapping can be removed in spring. The young figs which developed in the autumn are the most valuable. Although more new fruit will develop during the growing season, it will not always ripen. For the best development of the fruit, the tree must have a constant and uninterrupted supply of water, so it should be watered regularly. If a fig tree is planted in the right place, it will give pleasure for many years.

Ficus carica can also be grown indoors, although the leaves tend to be infested with red spider mite. A cold shower once a week, making sure that the bottoms of the leaves are particularly well drenched, can prevent

FICUS CARICA

this sort of infestation. Because of the large size of the leaves, a great deal of water evaporates, and it is important to ensure that the soil in the pot is always moist. The leaves will fall in the autumn and the plant can be placed in a cool spot with a temperature of approximately 5° C. and kept relatively dry. If necessary, re-pot the plant at the beginning of spring in a mixture consisting of two parts peat to one part potting compost, with some old, well-rotted manure.

The fig tree can be fairly easily propagated by taking cuttings. To do this, take fairly thin twigs about 20cm long, and push them halfway down into the soil when the leaves have fallen in the autumn. Like the mother tree, these twigs should be well covered during the winter. In the next growing season they will form roots, and the following year the young plants can be given a permanent spot in the garden.

Sycamore Fig

Scientific name: Ficus sycomorus L.
Family name: Moraceae
Natural habitat: southern Africa to Egypt and the Lebanon
English name: sycamore fig
Biblical name: sycamore fig

. . . But I was a shepherd, and I also took care of sycamore fig trees.
AMOS 7:14

The sycamore fig tree, which is mentioned less often in the Bible than the ordinary fig tree, was also very important in the region. Fully grown specimens reach a height of 15m and the branches can spread to approximately 40m in diameter. In some cases the circumference of the trunk is more than 7m. Thus, unlike the ordinary fig tree, *Ficus sycomorus* is a very impressive plant.

The fruit grows abundantly in large clusters, both on the new and on the old branches, and even on the old trunk. It is similar to the fruit of the ordinary fig tree, but often much smaller and of a poorer quality. It has a sweet taste and is eaten particularly by the poor people of the Bible lands.

Despite the fact that the wood of the sycamore fig is rather soft and porous, it keeps very well. The caskets for mummies made from this wood and found in Egyptian graves are still in good condition after more than 3,000 years. *Ficus sycomorus* is particularly common in Egypt. The wood is used for the manufacture of furniture, doors, chests etc.

GROWING TIPS
In cooler climates it is not possible to cultivate *Ficus sycomorus* outside all the year round. However, it can thrive in a tub and be left outside from early summer to the end of autumn, although it will rarely bear fruit.

The tree can produce fruit if it is planted in the open ground of a frost-free greenhouse. In this case it is best to cordon the tree by pruning it regularly and tying it back carefully. The first fruit will only appear on the old branches when the tree is quite old. It can be propagated by taking cuttings.

FICUS SYCOMORUS

Cotton

Scientific name:	Gossypium herbaceum L.
Family name:	Malvaceae
Natural habitat:	southern Europe, Mediterranean area, India and central Asia to central Africa
English name:	cotton
Biblical name:	linen

The garden had hangings of white and blue linen, fastened with cords of white linen and purple material . . .
ESTHER 1:6

In some translations the linen in Esther 1:6 is called cotton. According to a number of experts, that plant would be more appropriate for this passage. The account quoted above of the visit to King Ahasuerus's winter palace in Susa (598–596 BC) gives a good impression of the different materials available at that time.

Although cotton was only cultivated in Israel a few centuries before the birth of Christ, cotton materials had been traded for a long time before that. They came from India and Pakistan, where the cotton plant, *Gossypium*, was already being cultivated on a large scale. The genus consists of 20 to 40 different species and is a member of the mallow family (*Malvaceae*). A number of species, including *G. barbadense, G. hirsutum, G. arboreum,* and *G. herbaceum*, were cultivated on a large scale. These all have seeds with long hairs, and this fluff is the cotton. *G. arboreum and G. herbaceum* were the first species to be cultivated in the ancient world, and the fruit-bearing varieties which are cultivated on a large scale nowadays were developed, by a process of cross-fertilization and selection.

The species which was traditionally cultivated in the Holy Land is *Gossypium herbaceum*. This is a perennial plant, though it is grown as an annual. It has many branches, grows to a height of approximately 2m, and produces heart-shaped leaves with 3–7 lobes, and large yellow flowers with a purple heart. At a later stage the flowers turn a pinky red colour. After pollination, a fairly large fruit develops with 3–5 sections, enclosed in a fairly long dentate calyx, consisting of three sections. When it is ripe, the fruit bursts open and the fluff is expelled.

GROWING TIPS

Cotton seeds, which are available from a well-stocked seed merchant, should be sown indoors in early spring and raised indoors. It is best to sow the seed in a pot of soil rich in humus. Cover the seeds with an even layer of earth, and water well. Then cover this with a plastic bag. The seeds will germinate fairly quickly in this mini-greenhouse, and as soon as the two large seed leaves have developed, repot the plants into individual pots.

For healthy development, cotton plants need lots of nutrients and heat. The best results are produced with a mixture of equal parts of peat, potting compost and old, well-rotted stable manure. The plant needs lots of light, including some sun. Make sure that the soil is always thoroughly moist. Indoor plants are susceptible to whitefly.

When the plants have grown to a height of approximately 15cm, transplant them into a pot about 12cm wide. After three or four weeks some artificial fertilizer should be added to the water every ten days. When the large yellow flowers appear and have opened up completely, they should be fertilized by applying some pollen to the pistil by hand, using a brush. The fairly large triangular fruit will then develop from the flowers. It remains green for a long time and then bursts open to reveal the white cotton fluff.

Although cotton is a perennial plant, it is usually grown as an annual, as in the autumn it loses a lot of leaves and becomes rather unattractive and bare.

Ivy

Scientific name: Hedera helix L.
Family name: Araliaceae
Natural habitat: western, central and southern Europe
English name: ivy
Biblical name: ivy

And when the feast of Dionysus occurred they were forced to wear ivy wreaths and walk in the Dionysiac procession.
2 MACCABEES 6:7

The text quoted above undoubtedly refers to the ivy, *Hedera helix*. Presumably the Hebrews were not indignant about wearing ivy leaves as such, though they did feel humiliated by being compelled to enter the

temple of a heathen god and even to worship him. This event took place in about 165 BC, between the times of the Old and New Testaments.

Both the holly and the ivy have always played an important role in religious rites. For example, ivy was used by the Greeks in the worship of Bacchus. A section taken from a flowering branch loses its climbing properties, and the usual pointed shape of the leaves, consisting of three to five sections, is replaced by a perfect ellipse. This led them to believe that the leaves of a flowering branch cooled down the Bacchanalian passions summoned by the climbing leaves.

The yellowish-green flowers on their long stems are clustered together in a spherical umbel. The large black berries which are this plant's fruit are clustered in the same way. In the past, chemists sold ivy leaves to staunch the flow of blood, and the berries were used to treat fevers, constipation and gall or kidney stones.

GROWING TIPS

Hedera helix, which belongs to the Araliaceae family, is indigenous in many places. The plant is well-known as ground cover and as a climbing plant, and is very common in the woods of northern Europe. In order to encourage the stunted flowering form, it is grafted by horticulturalists onto the lower part of the stem of common ivy. Plants produced in this way grow into attractive round bushes which flower profusely and are covered in berries. Their scientific name is *Hedera helix* 'Arborescens' (syn. *H. arborea*). The common ivy plant is propagated by taking cuttings, which will easily take root, either in a glass of water, or in moist peat or garden soil. Later on they can be planted out in the garden. Ivy has few requirements as regards the composition of the soil. It will thrive in full sunlight or in the shade.

The cultivated varieties of common ivy, especially produced as pot plants, often have variegated or specially shaped leaves. They can also easily be propagated by taking cuttings in the same way as described above. When they have formed roots, the cuttings are potted in a soil mixture that is airy and rich in humus; for example, peat and old, well-rotted manure. In comparison with other pot plants, they grow reasonably well where there is little light.

The leaves are frequently infested with red spider mite in the dry atmosphere of the living-room. To prevent this, it is a good idea to spray the plant regularly with cold water.

Barley

Scientific name: Hordeum vulgare L.
Family name: Gramineae
Natural habitat: Europe
English name: barley
Biblical name: barley

The flax and barley were destroyed, since the barley had headed and the flax was in bloom.

EXODUS 9:31

Since time immemorial, many different varieties of barley have been cultivated throughout the world, and this plant is still one of the most important cereal crops. Not only is barley frequently mentioned in the Bible as a plant, but there are also many references to the products derived from it. As oats were not yet used for cattle feed, barley was also used for feeding donkeys, horses and other livestock.

Barley grows easily, even in arid soil, and ripens a month earlier than wheat. Originally three species were cultivated: *Hordeum distichon, H. vulgare,* and *H. hexastichon.* According to some researchers, the last of these was the most common in Biblical times, followed by *H. vulgare,* which was even grown in prehistoric times. In comparison with our modern fields of grain and their enormous yield per hectare, the harvest from the arid soil of the Holy Land was extremely meagre. In those times the seed was sown in the rainy season between November and March. Depending on the area and the type of soil, the first crop could be harvested in March or April.

GROWING TIPS

It is easy to grow barley yourself. If you sow the seed in spring it will flower in late summer or early autumn, depending on the variety, the place where it is sown, and obviously the weather. Barley has few requirements with regard to the composition of the soil, but the crop will be larger if the soil is rich in nutrients.

The ripe ears can be dried and used with other dried flowers to make attractive bouquets.

HORDEUM DISTICHON

Hyacinth

Scientific name: Hyacinthus orientalis L.
Family name: Liliaceae
Natural habitat: Mediterranean area, southwest Asia
English name: hyacinth
Biblical name: lily

Your two breasts are like two fawns, like twin fawns of a gazelle that browse among the lilies.
SONG OF SONGS 4:5

The 'lily' is probably the most common and the most controversial plant mentioned in the Bible. In the catalogue to the exhibition, 'Plants from the Bible', which was organized on the centenary of the Free University of Amsterdam in 1980, the organizer, M.H. van Es, wrote the following words on this subject:

'We have selected a narcissus *(Narcissus tazetta)* for

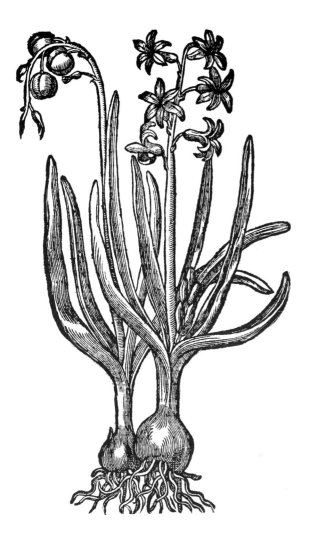

the 'Rose of Sharon' mentioned in the Song of Songs (2:1) although some people still believe that it should have been the tulip *(Tulipa montana)*. The same narcissus now flowers in the plains where Isaiah predicted salvation (Isaiah 35:1). The Church's idea about the parched land of the desert is not so appropriate now that roses are being raised in the sand in the nurseries of the Negev . . . Perhaps it is only a matter of time before we know exactly what flowers were meant by the 'lilies' which were a favourite in the Song of Songs (see above), and which are more splendid than Solomon, according to Christ (Matthew 6:28). Right now it is impossible to choose the most beautiful from the dozens of bright coloured flowers which adorn the fields and which have all been put forward as the winner in this beauty contest: *Adonis palestina, Anemone coronaria, Ranunculus asiaticus, Cyclamen persicum, Hyacinthus orientalis, Nymphaea lotus, Iris pseudacorus, Lilium candidum* and all the others we would like you to enjoy. Perhaps we will never know, for the Bible poses this sort of problem of identification more than once.'

Certainly it is a very confusing matter. When the temperature rises in spring and a fresh shower falls, the slopes of the hills of Israel are covered with all sorts of flowers, any of which could be the lily of the Bible. In themselves, they are all equally splendid. Many of the plants which have been called lilies are easy to grow in a cooler climate. Many people buy a bunch of anemones in spring *(Anemone coronaria)*. It may not generally be known that these popular flowers can be grown in any garden. The bulbs can be bought very cheaply, and planted either in spring (to flower in the summer), or in the autumn (to flower in the spring). The Persian buttercup *Ranunculus asiaticus* can be grown in the same way.

The bulbs of *Cyclamen hederifolium,* which has slightly smaller flowers than the well-known *Cyclamen persicum* and various other related hardy varieties, are also generally available. They will thrive in well-drained soil, rich in humus, provided they are protected from too much rain, for example, with a pane of glass.

Hyacinths are also sold in large numbers in every colour and variety, although they are usually selections of the original wild *Hyacinthus orientalis.*

The autumn crocus, *Colchicum autumnale,* is a species which is very similar to the species which grow in Israel. It is found growing wild throughout Europe. The autumn crocus is on sale everywhere from midsummer onwards, and will even flower without water on the windowsill. When it has finished flowering, the bulb can be put in the garden and planted about 10 cm below the ground in a shaded spot. In the spring it will produce a great deal of leaf, and in the autumn the crocus-like flowers will appear. There are many hybrids of this plant on the market, with flowers in various sizes.

Although the original hyacinth, *Hyacinthus orientalis,* is rarely grown, many millions of bulbs from a large variety of cultivars are sold by specialist bulb growers every year. Hyacinths are so popular that for most people it is not really necessary to describe how to grow them. However, a short description is given below for anyone who would find it useful.

Plant the bulbs in the autumn and the hyacinths will flower from late spring to early summer, depending on the weather. Although the reserves of nutrients in the bulb itself mean that the hyacinth will develop well in any type of soil, a fertile, well-drained sandy soil is best. To ensure that you have bulbs which will flower every year, it is a good idea to feed them with some artificial fertilizer a month after planting them. Repeat this in the spring when the tips of the bulbs appear above the ground and after they have flowered. Remove the heads when they have flowered to prevent seeds setting, which takes a lot of strength from the bulb. As soon as the foliage has died, dig up the bulbs and keep them in a dry, not too cold place until they are ready to be planted out again in the autumn.

Hyacinths are propagated by means of lateral buds. A method often used by bulb growers is to cut or hollow out the fully grown hyacinth bulbs which will produce a large number of lateral buds after a special heat treatment. These can then be cultivated themselves as flowering bulbs. However, this is a specialist task, best left to the experts.

There are other bulbs and corms which could be included amongst the many different lilies of the field. 2 Kings 6:25 reads: 'There was a great famine in the city; the siege lasted so long that a donkey's head sold for eighty shekels of silver and a fourth of a cab of seed pods for five shekels.' The 'cab [a measure] of seed pods' refers to a bulb of a species of *Ornithogalum,* which we know as Star of Bethlehem. However, it is not the pot plant with white or light blue flowers also known by this name, because this belongs to the genus *Campanula,* and has nothing to do with the plants mentioned in the Bible. The bulbs concerned here are probably *Ornithogalum narbonense,* which are edible, in contrast with other indigenous species which are poisonous. It is worth planting these Star of Bethlehem bulbs yourself. After several years they develop into attractive plants with white, star-shaped flowers which grow in umbels and truly live up to their name.

Yellow Iris

Scientific name: Iris pseudacorus L.
Family name: Iridaceae
Natural habitat: western Europe, northern Africa
English name: yellow iris
Biblical name: lily

I will be like the dew to Israel; he will blossom like a lily . . .
HOSEA 14:5

Although it is extremely difficult to say which species of plants can really be included amongst the lilies and the flowers of the field, some people consider that the yellow iris *(Iris pseudacorus)* is a likely candidate.

When it is flowering, this striking plant can be seen from a long way away because of its many bright yellow flowers.

The yellow iris is a common indigenous plant in many parts of Europe as well as in the Holy Land. It often grows in large numbers in marshy spots, particularly along the water's edge next to calamus and burr reeds, which are difficult to tell apart from it when they are not flowering. In early summer flowering stalks appear between the broad, sword-shaped leaves which are 2–3cm wide and up to 100cm long. The large yellow flowers open a few at a time. They flower for only one or two days and then develop large, long, green seed pods, rather like gherkins.

As soon as the triangular fruit is ripe, it bursts open and the oily, golden brown seeds are visible, lying neatly in a row like a pile of draughts. They fall in the water and float along with the current or are carried away by the wind, eventually settling in the mud to germinate the following spring.

In heraldry, the iris *(Iris germanica)* plays an important role as a stylized symbol. The shield used by King Clovis of France in the battle against the Huns was decorated with this flower. The emblem became the symbol of Christianity during the Crusade of 1137, led by Louis VII, when the flower became known as the 'fleur de Louis' (flower of Louis), which later became the 'fleur de luce' (flower of light), then changed to 'fleur de lys', and finally became the present-day 'fleur de lis'.

In 1179 the fleur de lis was first used in the coat-of-arms of the King of France. It consisted of a blue field with a large number of 'fleur de lis' motifs. At that time, royal garments and ecclesiastical objects were all decorated with lilies. Subsequently the fleur de lis continued to form part of the coat of arms of the French nation.

GROWING TIPS

It is very easy to grow the yellow iris from seed. It is best to use fresh seeds. Sow them in a small pot of ordinary garden soil, or in a moist spot in the garden. They will gradually start to germinate in the spring and then develop into large plants in the course of the summer. Do not expect any flowers to appear in the first year after sowing the seeds: you will have to wait another year. Although the yellow iris thrives best in mud or along the water's edge, it will also flourish in normal garden soil, as long as it is not too dry.

IRIS PSEUDACORUS

Woad

Scientific name: Isatis tinctoria L.
Family name: Cruciferae
Natural habitat: central and southern Europe, Asia
English name: woad
Biblical name: purple (linen)

The merchants of the earth will weep and mourn over her because no one buys their cargoes anymore—cargoes of gold, silver, precious stones and pearls; fine linen, purple, silk and scarlet cloth; every sort of citron wood, and articles of every kind made of ivory, costly wood, bronze, iron and marble; cargoes of cinnamon and spice, of incense, myrrh and frankincense, of wine and olive oil, of fine flour and wheat; cattle and sheep; horses and carriages; and bodies and souls of men.

REVELATION 18:11–13

It is virtually certain that woad, which is indigenous to many parts of northern Europe and is known as *Isatis tinctoria* was used in Biblical times for dyeing linen and wool. The extracts from some plants can be used to produce different colours, depending on how they are prepared. Woad is one of the plants in this category. When it is boiled, this plant produces a yellow or orange colour. If some parts of the plant are left to ferment, they produce a blue colouring agent. This dye was known to the ancient Greeks and Romans, and was extremely important for many centuries. Following the discovery of the sea route to India, it lost its value when indigo was imported from the Far East as a product of *Indigofera tinctoria*. Later still, the dye was prepared synthetically.

The natural habitat of the genus *Isatis*, which comprises about 45 different species, covers Europe, the Mediterranean, and the Near and Far East. Of all these species, *Isatis tinctoria* is most commonly used as a dye.

It belongs to the *Cruciferae* family, but has a rather special place in this family. Unlike other *Cruciferae*, which form fruit with several seeds divided by partitions, woad forms a fruit with a single seed.

In the cooler parts of Europe, *Isatis tinctoria* is extremely rare, at least growing in the wild. It is a biennial—and sometimes a perennial—plant which will grow to a height of 60cm, although specimens may reach a height of 150cm depending on the conditions. The plant has bluish-green, arrow-shaped leaves surrounding the stem. The small yellow flowers form loose composite clusters. Later the striking, hanging, dark brown single seed fruit develops on these. The fruit-bearing stem continues to be attractive for a long time if it is cut down shortly after the fruit has turned brown.

GROWING TIPS
Woad is fairly easy to grow from seed. Sow the seeds in late summer or autumn, and the plants will develop before winter to flower in the summer of the following year. Woad is tolerant of any type of soil. However, if you want to make sure of having good flowers it is advisable to sow new plants every year.

ISATIS TINCTORIA

Walnut

Scientific name: Juglans regia L.
Family name: Juglandaceae
Natural habitat: Europe
English name: walnut
Biblical name: nut

---

*I went down to the grove of nut trees to look at the new growth in
the valley, to see if the vines had budded or the pomegranates were
in bloom.*

SONG OF SONGS 6:11

The walnut, *Juglans regia*, which belongs to the walnut
family Juglandaceae, originates from an area which
extends from south-east Europe to central Asia.
Although it was only introduced to Europe in the
second half of the sixteenth century, the walnut is now
one of the most common nuts to be cultivated on a
large scale. As a result, walnut trees can nowadays be
found in virtually all the temperate regions of the
world. These days, France, Italy, Romania, California
and China produce and export the largest number of
nuts. Apart from the walnut, half a dozen other species
of *Juglans* are specially cultivated for their edible nuts.

Various different species belonging to the *Juglans*
genus are cultivated, not only for their high quality
fruit, but also for their valuable wood which is both
beautiful and durable. For centuries this wood has been
used in the furniture industry, particularly to make
splendid chests and cupboards. The smooth, straight-
grained wood of the trunk has a warm colour and a
beautiful natural glow which is described as the nut
wood, while the inner heartwood has complex patterns
and is known as root wood. Both are highly prized.

Fully grown specimens of Juglans regia can grow to
a height of about 30m. They have a thick crown of
countless rather large leaves between 5 and 12cm long,
with smooth edges, arranged in a characteristic pattern.

The leaf of the walnut tree develops rather late
compared to that of other deciduous trees. Before the
tree is completely in leaf, the single monoecious
inflorescence appears on the twigs which grew the year
before. The countless male flowers which contain the
pollen form rather thick, hanging green catkins. Like
the alder and the hazel, walnut trees are pollinated by
the wind. The female flowers sometimes grow on their
own, but are usually in clusters of catkins on the new
shoots of the same tree. They are fertilized by the
pollen, which is blown on to the two short pistils. The
nuts, known botanically as drupes, grow from these.

JUGLANS REGIA

They reach a length of 4–5cm and are comparable to the almond and the peach.

The word 'nut' is not really correct from a botanical point of view, for a nut such as a hazelnut is a dry fruit with a brittle shell which is not enclosed by soft flesh. Walnuts have a thick casing and a hard shell. The kernel or seed is the edible part of the nut. It is formed by two grooved and folded seed lobes, and is almost 50 per cent oil. Like the leaves and casing of the fruit, the brown skin of the seed contains a great deal of tannin. Some people believe that because of this tannin in the fallen leaves, it is impossible for other vegetation to survive in the vicinity of the tree.

Although the walnut tree is fairly resistant to low temperatures in winter, the tree is very sensitive to frost when the leaves come out. Fairly often, all the young leaves and the flowers are completely destroyed when there is a slight frost. Over the centuries people have developed strains which bud later and produce high yields. However, in cooler climates, frost is always a threat.

A great deal of superstition surrounds the walnut, and there are countless legends about it. The Greeks offered walnuts to their goddess Artemis, who controlled fertility. For the Romans the nuts also symbolized fertility, and during a marriage feast the nuts would be cast amongst the wedding guests. In the Middle Ages it was believed that evil spirits and the devil were concealed in the branches of the walnut tree.

GROWING TIPS

Sow the seeds outside in late spring. Place the nuts on their sides and then cover them with a layer of soil the depth of the nut itself. Even if they are sown late, the germinating seeds can be damaged by ground frost, so it is best to cover them as a preventative measure.

The seeds germinate slowly and in an irregular fashion. Once the seedlings have developed, they can be transplanted. They will thrive best in a warm and sheltered spot in nutritious, well-drained soil which is fairly rich in calcium. The young plants grow vigorously, but at this stage they are still very delicate and need to be tied back regularly to supporting canes.

The advantage of growing a walnut tree from seed yourself is that you can choose how it will grow—as a bush, a dwarf or a standard tree. You influence its shape by removing the crown of the tree when it has grown to the desired height. The pruned sapling will then start to branch out at various points.

Juniper

Scientific name: Juniperus oxycedrus L.
Family name: Cupressaceae
Natural habitat: Mediterranean area to Syria and Iran
English name: juniper
Biblical name: algum

Send me also cedar, pine and algum logs from Lebanon, for I know that your men are skilled in cutting timber there.

2 CHRONICLES 2:8

Hiram's ships brought gold from Ophir; and from there they brought great cargoes of almug wood and precious stones. The King used the almug wood to make supports for the temple of the Lord.

I KINGS 10:11–12

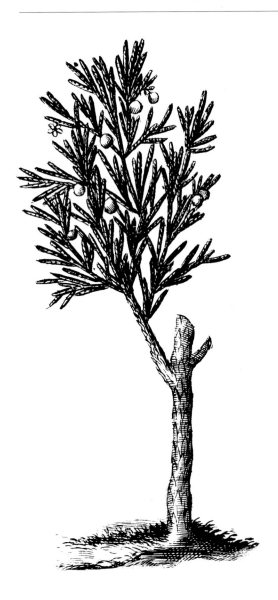

There does not seem to be any reason to suppose that algum wood and almug wood are from different trees. In fact, the different names both refer to a single tree; the different spellings probably exist because the authors of the Bible did not know exactly how to spell the foreign name of this timber, which was clearly imported from outside Israel. In the course of time this confusion has increased. However, as algum wood is referred to in the same breath as the wood of cedars and cypresses, and as it was highly valued for making furniture, it makes sense to assume that this wood belongs to the group of conifers which still grew in the Holy Land on a fairly large scale in Bible times. The fact that hard, sweet-smelling wood was not produced by many other indigenous trees at this time gives added credence to this theory.

The conifers which are mentioned in the Bible by name for their durable wood include the cedar, the cypress, the parasol pine and the Aleppo pine. The slightly less common juniper or *Juniperus* can be added to this list of soft woods. The species which are found in the Holy Land include *J. drupacea*, *J. excelsa*, *J. oxycedrus* and *J. phoenicea*. *J. excelsa* in particular is a juniper which grows to a considerable size and produces excellent timber of no lesser quality or fragrance than the other coniferous trees mentioned above. As a result of deforestation and erosion in Bible lands over the course of the centuries, very few large specimens of the various *Juniperus* species mentioned above have survived. Efforts are being made to keep the remaining specimens alive, and new trees are being planted.

GROWING TIPS

Juniperus oxycedrus, like the other junipers mentioned above, is not hardy in cooler climates. It can be grown in a tub, which means that it can grow outside in summer and spend the winter indoors, protected from frost at a temperature of 5° C.

Obviously there are other species of *Juniperus* which do very well in the cold. An example is *Juniperus communis*, but there are many other species cultivated for the garden.

Juniperus can be propagated from seed or by taking cuttings.

Lettuce

Scientific name: Lactuca sativa L.
Family name: Compositae
Natural habitat: Europe
English name: lettuce
Biblical name: bitter herbs

... together with unleavened bread and bitter herbs.
NUMBERS 9:11

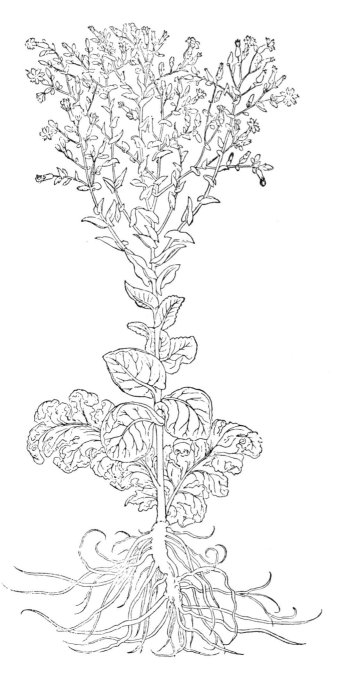

The lettuce plant, *Lactuca sativa*, which is cultivated today in many forms with different colours and different leaves, is very different from the original variety in many respects. This was one of the larger groups of plants referred to in the Bible by the phrase 'bitter herbs'. The origin of *Lactuca sativa* is not known, but there is no doubt that the plant has been cultivated since ancient times. It is an annual which grows vertically, and has dense foliage on the stalks, which can grow to a height of 60–100cm when the plant is flowering. Before the plant flowers, the soft leaves sometimes form a sort of loose head.

The inflorescence can be umbelliferous or plumed, and consists of large numbers of small yellow flowers. The big, flat seeds which develop in large quantities when the plant has been fertilized, have a characteristic greyish or white colour.

The bitter taste has disappeared in the course of the ages as a result of cross-pollination and selection, and consequently the plant has increased enormously in popularity. There are now many different varieties on the market, and some of these have such beautiful leaves that they would not be out of place in an ornamental garden.

GROWING TIPS

Anyone can grow lettuce. There is an enormous range of varieties available from seed merchants. If you sow them in spring, the different varieties will develop in 6–8 weeks into beautiful, well-formed plants. In order to ensure that you will have fully grown plants suitable for consumption throughout the summer well into autumn it is a good idea to make new sowings every three weeks. If the heads of lettuce are to be really full, it is important to manure the soil well. Half-grown plants also thrive on some extra artificial fertilizer.

Bay Tree

Scientific name:	Laurus nobilis L.
Family name:	Lauraceae
Natural habitat:	Mediterranean area
English name:	bay tree
Biblical name:	green tree

LAURUS NOBILIS

I have seen a wicked and ruthless man flourishing like a green tree in its native soil.

PSALMS 37:35

Although the 'flourishing...green tree' and the Greek name which translates 'cedar of Lebanon' may not be directly associated with the bay, people who have seen this tree in its natural habitat will understand why these names have been given. This woody plant forms many roots, creating impenetrable thickets which choke any other vegetation, and older specimens may resemble a cedar seen from afar. It is certainly strange to note that the authors of the Bible never mention the bay in so many words, although it grows profusely throughout the Holy Land and the Mediterranean area.

This deciduous evergreen can reach a height of 20m. The leathery leaves are long and oval, and when they are bruised, they emit a strong fragrance which many people find attractive. When the greenish-white flowers have been pollinated, monocotyledonous black fruits the size of an olive develop. Oil pressed from this fruit was used for medicinal purposes; there is a story that the Emperor Nero (37–68) had his apartments perfumed with the ethereal oils of the bay leaf during epidemics, in order to avoid being infected.

The bay, a type of laurel, became even better known because of the laurel crown used by the Greeks and Romans to crown their athletes during the Olympic Games, held from 776 BC.

Nowadays, the bay leaf is a well-known culinary herb. The bay tree is also cultivated as an ornamental plant, and used for many other purposes.

GROWING TIPS

In cooler climates, *Laurus nobilis* is a non-hardy plant. However, during some recent severe winters, it became clear that the bay tree could tolerate more frost than was previously supposed. If the shrub is planted out in a protected spot, with little sun, particularly during the winter period, it can survive temperatures as low as -20°C. If you do not have such a spot, it is a good idea to bring the bay tree into a frost-free place for the winter. Over the years, beautiful plants can be grown in tubs which can easily be pruned into all sorts of shapes.

As in the natural state, cultivated specimens also tolerate drought well. Young shoots, which will wilt as a result of a water shortage, will quickly be restored when they are watered. In the summer, when the bay tree grows outdoors, feed the plant every two weeks with artificial fertilizer. If necessary, you can repot the plants into new soil rich in nutrients, consisting of two parts of peat to one part of potting compost and one part of well-rotted manure. Prune the tree by hand twice a year in order to maintain its original shape. As soon as the young shoots reach a length of 6–8cm, usually in early summer, prune back to the newly-formed leaf. Then prune them a second time in late summer.

In a hot, dry environment, bay trees are sometimes ravaged by cottony maple scale. This can be treated with a ball of cotton wool soaked in methylated spirits. The bay tree is also prone to red spider mite in these conditions. The best remedy for this is to douse the leaves every week with cold water.

Propagate the plant by taking cuttings, which will take root with the help of a rooting preparation if the soil is warmed to a temperature of 20–23°C. It can also be grown from seed, but the olive-sized seeds germinate slowly, and only at high temperatures of 20–30°C.

Lentil

Scientific name: Lens culinaris Medicus
Family name: Leguminosae
Natural habitat: central, southern and eastern Europe
English name: lentil
Biblical name: lentil

---

*Once when Jacob was cooking some stew, Esau came in from the
open country, famished. He said to Jacob, 'Quick, let me have
some of that red stew ! I'm famished!' (That is why he was also
called Edom). Jacob replied, 'First sell me your birthright.'
'Look, I am about to die,' Esau said, 'What good is the birthright
to me?' But Jacob said, 'Swear to me first,' So he swore an oath
to him, selling his birthright to Jacob. Then Jacob gave Esau some
bread and some lentil stew. He ate bread and drank, and then
got up and left. So Esau despised his birthright.*

GENESIS 25:29–34

Lens culinarus (syn: *L. esculenta*) has the oldest and best-
known history of any pulse. It is an annual plant which
grows to a height of 15–40cm, with leaves ending in
tendrils. It belongs to the family Leguminosae and is
indigenous to southern Europe.

The plant has been cultivated since the Stone Age
for the great nutritional value of its seeds, which are rich
in protein, potassium and phosphorus. The pale, blue-
veined flowers have a white flag and are grouped
together in clusters of 1–3 flowers. When they have
been fertilized, they produce diamond-shaped, hairless
pods 2–3cm long, each containing only two flat lens-
shaped seeds the size of a small pea. The colour of these
seeds varies from a pale green or yellow to yellowish
brown and bleached black.

In the past they were highly valued as food,
although they are less popular today. Nevertheless,
lentils are still grown in virtually all the dry and
temperate regions, such as southern Europe, Asia, and
North Africa. They have remained an important part
of the traditional cooking of several countries, and are
now an established feature of international cuisine.

In addition to the plants which produce the seeds

LENS CULINARIS

in the colours described above, there is also a variety which produces red lentils. This variety is still widely grown nowadays in the poor soil of the Bible lands and it is almost certainly the variety which was used to prepare Jacob's dish.

In order to prepare soup or other dishes with lentils, they are soaked in water overnight before use, like all other pulses. Then they are boiled, though not for too long, as the aroma is in the skin. Provided they are kept in a cool, dark place, lentils will retain their taste for as long as five years. They can be mixed with barley and used to bake a type of bread which is particularly common in the poorer parts of Egypt.

GROWING TIPS

A keen gardener will have few problems growing lentils. Sow the seeds outside straight in the earth towards the end of spring or in the early summer. They will germinate quickly and grow into a fair sized plant in a short while, which will produce many ripe pods.

One hazard is that there is often too much rain during the months that the plant is ripening, and the plants are easily blown over. In addition, the plants, as well as the pods, will easily rot if they are grown too close together.

Madonna Lily

Scientific name: Lilium candidum L.
Family name: Liliaceae
Natural habitat: Mediterranean area
English name: Madonna lily
Biblical name: lily

I will be like the dew to Israel; he will blossom like a lily . . .
HOSEA 14:5

LILIUM CANDIDUM

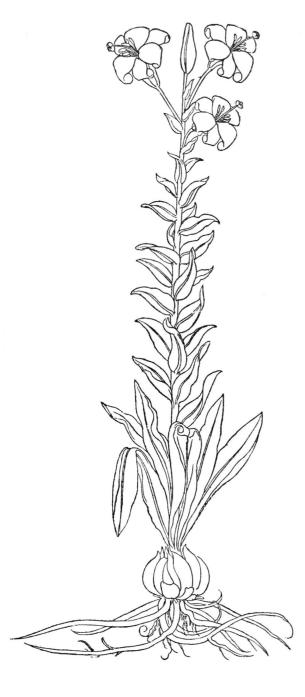

Although there is some doubt as to whether the Madonna lily is really a Bible plant, this flower has become so closely connected with the Christian religion over the centuries that it should not be left out here. The bulb of this plant consists of many fleshy scuta which develop into large quantities of even, green foliage at the beginning of the autumn. These remain throughout the winter. In the spring, a flowering stalk develops approximately 1m tall, and, depending on the size of the bulb, one or more beautiful white, trumpet-like flowers grow on this stalk, emitting a strong fragrance. The longer the bulbs remain in the same place, the more flowering stalks will grow.

GROWING TIPS

If you use bulbs, which are readily available from a well-stocked bulb grower, they should be planted in fertile soil during the dormant period, which falls during the summer months in northern Europe. The tip of the bulb should be just below the surface of the soil. The plants develop best in alkaline soil, but will also thrive in other types of soil, if the drainage is good. Although Madonna lilies may seem easy to grow because they are so widespread, it is not always easy to obtain healthy virus-free stock of *Lilium candidum*. The foliage should be a pure and even green. If the leaves have yellowish marks or stripes, this means that it has been attacked by a virus which cannot be eradicated. Diseased plants will not flower, or will hardly flower at all, and are a threat to other plants which are sensitive to viruses. It is therefore best to destroy them.

You can propagate the plant by dividing up the bulbs. New plants can also be cultivated from seed, though it will take 6–8 years before the first flowers finally appear.

Flax

Scientific name: Linum usitatissimum L.
Family name: Linaceae
Natural habitat: Europe, the Orient
English name: flax
Biblical name: flax

She selects wool and flax and works with eager hands.
PROVERBS 31:13

Flax, which is mentioned many times in the Bible, is one of the oldest fibrous plants from which linen is woven. The genus consists of approximately 230 species belonging to the Linaceae family which grow wild in temperate and sub-tropical regions, and especially in the Mediterranean area. The cultivation of flax for the production of linen is very old and goes back more than seven thousand years. In Biblical times various different products were made from flax such as linen cloths (John 13:4), shrouds and grave cloths (John 11:44), shawls (Isaiah 3:23) and linen (Ezekiel 40:3). In Egypt, flax was an important crop, and in Canaan it was also well known before the arrival of the Israelites (Joshua 2:6). During services in the temple, priests wore only linen garments. The combination of wool and linen signified evil to the Jews (Leviticus 19:19; Deuteronomy 22:11).

Although there were several flaxes suitable for the production of linen, the main species grown was *Linum usitatissimum*. This annual plant with only one stalk is of unknown origin, as are so many uncultivated plants. It grows to a length of more than 100cm; the leaves are bluish-green in colour and lanciform. The white or blue flowers are 1 to 1.5cm across and grow in a loosely arranged umbel. The five petals are little longer than sepals. They soon finish flowering, and are blown away by the slightest breath of wind. The round box-shaped fruits, each the size of a small pea, grow at the end of the stem and contain many flat brown seeds. As soon as these are wet they exude a sticky substance. Linseed oil is pressed from this seed, which is also known as linseed. It is a strong unsaturated drying oil used in the paint and varnish industry. When the oil has been extracted, the remainder is processed as cattle food in the form of linseed cake or linseed flour.

Flax is harvested as soon as it turns yellow at the end of the growing season. In former times it was then laid out to dry on the roofs so that the woody stalks separated easily in the sunshine and the fibres could be pulled apart. Later on this process—also known as 'retting'—was also carried out by rotting the flax in ditches. After the retting process, the woody parts of the stalks were broken into small pieces. During this 'scutching' process part of the bark fibre broke away.

Nowadays the flax is retted mechanically. After the retting process the fibres are processed further, and can then be spun into linen.

GROWING TIPS

In order to grow really well, flax requires rich and nutritious soil. This is why a good harvest is produced when it is cultivated in a heavy clay soil. The varieties which are grown particularly for their beautiful flowers also thrive in lighter soils. Sow the seeds in summer in a sunny spot where the plants are to grow.

Flax is an attractive ornamental plant. Some particularly beautiful varieties of *Linum grandiflorum* are available. These produce abundant fruit as well as flowering profusely. The fruits have long stalks which can be cut and then slowly dried. They are then suitable to use for making attractive dried bouquets.

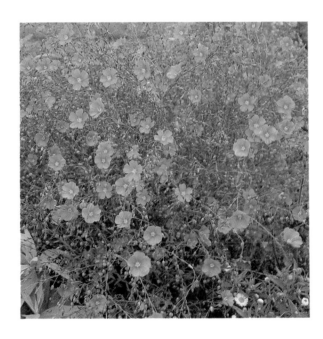

LINUM USITATISSIMUM

Oriental Amber Tree

Scientific name: Liquidambar orientalis Miller
Family name: Hamamelidaceae
Natural habitat: Asia Minor
English name: Oriental amber tree
Biblical name: myrrh

---

*. . . and saw a caravan of Ishmaelites coming from Gilead.
Their camels were loaded with spices, balm and myrrh . . .*
GENESIS 37:25

This text clearly identifies Gilead as a place where spices, balm and myrrh were traded. It provides a clue to the exact meaning of the instructions about incense given to Moses, Exodus 30:34. The gum resin spoken of there might well have come from the *Liquidambar orientalis,* as well as being derived from the *Storax* tree.

In those days amber trees grew in the area around Gilead in the northwest of Israel. Nowadays they are only found in a few parts of Asia Minor, where some grow to a height of 15 to 30m.

In addition to the *Liquidambar orientalis* referred to here, which is not hardy in cooler climates, there are five other species, of which *Liquidambar styraciflua* is the best known. This variety is indigenous to the central and eastern regions of the United States, Mexico and Guatemala. In these areas the tree can develop to gigantic proportions, over 50m tall. These giant trees are by no means rare in the Atlantic States of North America, for example, in the swamps of Florida.

However, they never grow to this sort of height in Europe.

The tree grows in a characteristic pyramid shape and is easily identified by the splendid carmine colours which appear in the late autumn. The leaves are very similar to those of the plane tree and the ash. They are fairly large and palmate, with five to seven serrated lobes. The male flowers grow in 'ears' while the female flowers develop as a spherical inflorescence. The fruits, which are produced at the end of the season, grow at the end of long stems and are spherical. The young annual shoots have a beautiful striking red colour which contrasts vividly with the dull grey of the older branches. The latter are often covered in a layer of cork, which is especially visible in winter, when the leaves have been shed.

The name of the genus *Liquidambar* is derived from the Latin words *liquido* (liquid) and *ambar* (amber). Amber is a scent which was particularly valuable in the past. It is found in the bodies of sperm whales and other cetaceans, in the form of ambergris. Therefore, as its name indicates, *Liquidambar* produces liquid resin which smells of amber. The name of the species *styraciflua* is derived from the Latin word *styrax,* (storax) and *fluere,* (to drip). In America this tree is popularly known as the sweet gum.

Apart from its fragrant resin, which is used in the pharmaceutical and perfume industries, the tree also produces high quality timber of great strength.

GROWING TIPS

As mentioned above, *Liquidambar orientalis* is a species which can only survive in climates with very little or no frost. On the other hand, *Liquidambar styraciflua* tolerates frost very well. Although this tree will never grow as tall in our own gardens as it does in its natural habitat, it can still grow to a respectable height. The tree usually thrives in any soil which retains moisture, provided it is not too shallow and does not contain too much chalk. As a mature tree can grow to an enormous size, it is not suitable for a small garden. It comes into its own best as a solitary tree, for example, in the middle of a large lawn. The most striking characteristic of *Liquidambar styraciflua* is its autumn colouring: some years it will turn a beautiful purplish red.

The plant can be propagated from seed or by means of layering. Young plants and older specimens of this species cultivated from cuttings are also available in garden centres.

LIQUIDAMBAR STYRACIFLUA

Thorn Bush

Scientific name: Lycium barbarum L.
Family name: Solanaceae
Natural habitat: Mediterranean area, Portugal
English name: thorn bush
Biblical name: thorn bush

The thorn bush said to the trees, 'If you really want to anoint me king over you, come and take refuge in my shade; but if not, then let fire come out of the thorn-bush and consume the cedars of Lebanon!'

JUDGES 9:15

Nettles, thorns and thistles are mentioned frequently in the Bible. In fact, they are mentioned so frequently that in some cases it is not always possible to ascertain exactly which plants are meant. As the thorn bush has a very large natural habitat and is also found in the Holy Land, it is reasonable to assume that the Bible writers had it in mind. *Lycium barbarum*,—the scientific name of the thorn bush—is also indigenous in northern Europe. It can develop to become an impenetrable bush about 3m in height. In sandy dunes, where this member of the nightshade family (Solanaceae) is often found, it is particularly striking during the autumn. When the violet-coloured flowers have been fertilized, large numbers of berry-like fruit develop on the one-year-old branches. When they have ripened, they turn red and are clearly visible. In addition, the thorns on the older branches are striking, and it is precisely because of these thorns that this bush is often planted to form a hedge in Mediterranean areas. Both the stems and the long greyish-green leaves tolerate the salty soil and the sea winds very well. At the end of the season the leaves turn yellow, contrasting attractively with the red berries. Although the fruit is poisonous for humans, birds eat it greedily.

GROWING TIPS

Thorn bushes are very easy to grow from seed. The ripe berries contain several flat, light brown seeds which can be pressed out. The contents are then washed, and the clean seeds dried.

They germinate best the following spring. You can sow them in a pot fairly early in the season. As long as the seeds were ripe when they were harvested and the outside temperature is high enough, they will germinate within a few weeks. When the plants have been re-potted once or twice, they can be planted out in the garden.

The thorn bush is not at all particular with regard to the type of soil in which it grows, but the more nutrients there are in the soil, the more prolifically it will flourish.

LYCIUM BARBARUM

Broom

Scientific name:	Lygos raetam (Forskal) Heywood
Family name:	Leguminosae
Natural habitat:	northern Africa, southwest Asia
English name:	broom
Biblical name:	broom tree

... while he himself went a day's journey into the desert. He came to a broom tree, sat down under it and prayed that he might die ...

1 KINGS 19:4

The broom tree referred to in this text at first glance closely resembles other types of broom which are common in gardens. However, from the botanical point of view, it is quite a different plant. Though it belongs to the same family (Leguminosae), this variety belongs to a completely different genus, *Lygos*. *Lygos raetam*, the official scientific name of this variety of broom (an out-of-date but better-known synonym is *Retama raetam*) is not hardy in cooler winters.

The bush, which can grow to a height of approximately 2m, has dense branches and thin, springy twigs. The rather small, long leaves are covered in thick hair. They soon fall off and are not very significant. The shrub becomes much more beautiful when it blooms profusely after the rainy season. The flowers are white and about 1.5cm in diameter. They later turn a creamy colour. When the bush is in full bloom, the flowers emit a pleasantly sweet fragrance and attract large numbers of insects. The flowering branches are sometimes cut and imported to be sold as cut flowers. Occasionally they are also artificially dyed pink or lilac.

GROWING TIPS

It is quite easy to cultivate *Lygos raetam* in temperate climates in a tub, kept outside from early summer through to autumn. It develops best in a strong mixture of soil composed of equal parts of peat, potting compost and old, well-rotted manure. You can prevent the plant from developing into a weak, unsightly specimen which flowers poorly—if at all—by always placing it in a light and sunny spot. As the flowers form on the young twigs which are only a year old, it is essential to prune the bush every year.

The easiest way to propagate it is from seed, but it is also possible to take cuttings. It is possible to order young plants from a few well-stocked nurseries.

LYGOS RAETAM

Mandragora

Scientific name: Mandragora autumnalis Bertol.;
                  Mandragora officinarum L.
Family name: Solanaceae
Natural habitat: Mediterranean area, central Europe
                  and southern Portugal
English name: mandragora
Biblical name: mandrake

MANDRAGORA OFFICINARUM

During wheat harvest, Reuben went out into the fields and found some mandrake plants, which he brought to his mother Leah. Rachel said to Leah, 'Please give me some of your son's mandrakes.' But she said to her, 'Wasn't it enough that you took away my husband? Will you take my son's mandrakes too?' 'Very well,' Rachel said, 'he can sleep with you tonight in return for your son's mandrakes.' 'So when Jacob came in from the fields that evening, Leah went out to meet him. 'You must sleep with me,' she said. 'I have hired you with my son's mandrakes.' So he slept with her that night.

GENESIS 30:14–16

Mandragora belongs to the nightshade family (*Solanaceae*), and is found mainly in the Mediterranean area, but can also be found to the east as far as the Himalayas. *Mandragora officinarum* is the mandrake plant of legend. It has virtually no stem, and large fleshy roots. The leaves of the plant are up to 30cm long with indented edges. They are long and lanciform or oval in shape, and grow in a rosette until the plant flowers. In the spring, short-stemmed, yellowish-white, bell-shaped flowers appear, which later turn a bluish colour.

When the plant has flowered, oval berries the size of a plum develop. They are green at first and later turn yellow. These are the 'apples of love' referred to in the Bible. They grow together in the middle of the rosette of leaves, like eggs in a nest. When they are ripe, the leaves turn yellow and finally die off. The ripe yellow fruit emits a sweet fragrance and is edible.

The mandrake is particularly interesting because of the many ancient legends it has inspired. Even in the Old Testament, the fruit is mentioned as bringing good luck, as revealed in the passages quoted above. In ancient times, the thick root had a considerable reputation as a medicine, a magic potion or a talisman which brought good luck. The roots contain toxins which have an anaesthetizing effect. An extract of mandrake roots was therefore used in operations and for other medical purposes.

During the Middle Ages the root, which rather resembles the outline of the human body because of its shape, was often carved into a 'mandrake man', an amulet intended to bring its owner wealth, fertility and protection against all sorts of ills and evil spirits. Such mandrake men were very scarce and much coveted, so they were extremely valuable. For some time it was believed that the mandrake plant only grew in places where someone had been crucified, and where the blood of the crucified person had dripped onto the earth. This had supposedly given the root its shape of a human body. Digging up the mandrake root was also a task surrounded by magic. It had to be done at night, in the presence of a dog who had to be tied to the plant and was not allowed to survive the ceremony. As the plant supposedly emitted a ghastly shriek when it was dug up, those who were present had to stop their ears beforehand. As the real mandrake was so rare and valuable, imitation mandrake men were also made from the roots of other plants such as bryony (*Bryonia*), the wild onion (*Allium victorialis*), and the wild carrot (*Daucus*).

GROWING TIPS

The mandrake is a rare plant, and is only occasionally found even in botanical collections. In regions with a temperate climate, the plant is reasonably hardy in winter, and can be cultivated if some care is taken. The plant needs rich, well-drained soil and a sunny spot. During the winter months, the root should be protected against frost, perhaps with a mulch of leaves or straw.

The mandrake can be propagated from seed. The fairly large, flat seeds are removed from the berries as soon as they start to shrivel up. When they have been cleaned and dried for a short while, they can be sown in the open soil. Plants will form even before winter, and after spending the winter under a layer of mulch, they will grow strongly in spring. The first flowers will only appear after about three years.

Mulberry

Scientific name:	Morus alba L.; Morus nigra L.
Family name:	Moraceae
Natural habitat:	southern and southeast Europe, China
English name:	mulberry
Biblical name:	mulberry tree

The apostles said to the Lord, 'Increase our faith!' He replied, 'If you have faith as small as a mustard seed, you can say to this mulberry tree, 'Be uprooted and planted in the sea', and it will obey you.

LUKE 17:5–6

The mulberry, like the well-known *Ficus*, belongs to the *Moraceae* family.

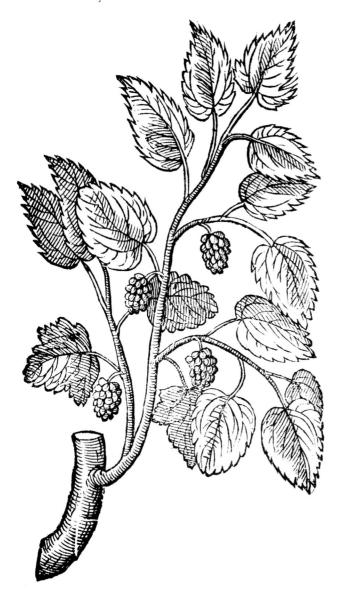

Probably imported from Iran, the black mulberry, *Morus nigra*, was grown in the Holy Land for its tasty fruit. The white mulberry, *Morus alba*, imported later from China and India, is still widely grown in Syria and Palestine for the silkworm industry. Over the years it has increasingly taken the place of the black mulberry. Although silkworms had been bred on mulberries in China since about 4000 BC, the Jews only used silk from about 600 BC. Incorrect interpretations in old Biblical translations meant that the word 'silk' was often used in places where linen was meant. This mistake is not found in modern versions.

The trees which Jesus saw were undoubtedly those of *Morus nigra*, as the breeding of silkworms on *Morus alba* took place much later in that part of the world. *Morus nigra* is a low, dense tree which grows to a height of about 10m and has a rough bark. The heart-shaped leaves are not usually indented. However, they are rough and have a coarsely serrated edge. The upper side has a dark green colour, while the bottom is a lighter colour and is covered in soft hair.

The mulberry tree does not bear fruit until it is mature. The fruit resembles large blackberries but is difficult to harvest and does not keep. Nevertheless, it is sometimes served as a dessert, and may be preserved in brandy. In the past, it was thought to have some pharmaceutical value.

The Greeks and Romans sometimes made mulberry wine. The reddish-purple juice of the fruit was also used to colour wine, and in the Middle Ages a good drink was made from it. A very strange use of the mulberry is referred to in the first book of Maccabees, 6:34. Here, fighting elephants are made more aggressive by painting their trunks with mulberry juice.

As the leaf of the white mulberry (*Morus alba*) is much softer, it is eminently suitable as food for the silkworm. *Morus alba* is a tree which grows to about 15m in height. It has leaves with irregular lobes which are only hairy on the underside. The fruit is white, though there are also varieties with red or black fruit. The wood of the white mulberry tree is yellowish, fairly hard and difficult to split. Because of its durability, it is used for furniture making. In the past it was used to make wagon wheels. It is highly suitable for skilled wood-turning, and is particularly beautiful when it is French-polished.

GROWING TIPS:

Despite their natural southerly habitat, both varieties of mulberry tree flourish in cooler climates. They are rarely cultivated for commercial purposes because the fruit is difficult to harvest and does not keep well. However, the mulberry is very suitable for growing in the garden and really comes into its own when it is trained against a south-facing wall. It does not have any special requirements with regard to the soil, and is easy to propagate from seed or by taking cuttings.

Myrtle

Scientific name: Myrtus communis L.
Family name: Myrtaceae
Natural habitat: Mediterranean area as far as Iran
English name: myrtle
Biblical name: myrtle

Instead of the thornbush will grow the pine tree, and instead of briers the myrtle will grow. This will be for the Lord's renown, for an everlasting sign, which will not be destroyed.

ISAIAH 55:13

Originally the myrtle (*Myrtus communis*) grew wild in Mediterranean countries as far as Iran. This woody plant was very common in Bible lands, particularly in the vicinity of Bethlehem and Hebron, as well as in the valleys of Mount Carmel and Tabor. In general, the myrtle, which belongs to the Myrtaceae family, grows as a shrub, but in some cases it can reach a height of some 5–8m.

The hard, valuable wood is sometimes used for making gymnastic equipment. The rather small, dark green, leathery leaves contain a fragrant volatile oil which is released when the leaves are damaged. In addition, the profuse white or light pink flowers are very striking because of their large numbers of stamens. They bloom from midsummer into late autumn. When they have been fertilized, large quantities of bluish-black, pea-sized berries form. These are used both in

MYRTUS
COMMUNIS

the perfume and in the pharmaceutical industries.

Over the centuries, myrtle has played a wide role in mythology and in the customs of different nations. As the myrtle is an evergreen, the Greeks considered it as a symbol of love and immortality. The leafy twigs were used by them to crown priests, heroes, and other leading figures. In Greek and Roman mythology, it was a sacred plant dedicated to Aphrodite and Venus.

In the Bible, myrtle was the symbol for peace, joy and justice. It was a very popular plant in the Middle East in ancient times, particularly among the Hebrews, who used the fragrant branches during the feast of Tabernacles to adorn their booths. (Nehemiah 8:16).

GROWING TIPS

Myrtus communis is not frost-hardy. Like many other woody plants which are mentioned in the Bible, it needs to be brought inside in winter. Between early summer and mid-autumn, move the myrtle outside, and dig it into the garden in a sunny spot. When the plant grows bigger, it can be placed in a tub on the verandah. Provided that it can be kept frost-free in a cool place in

the winter, it is a plant which will be a source of delight for a long time.

Myrtle can also be grown as an indoor pot plant, provided it is placed in a light spot which is not too warm. If the temperature is too high and the relative humidity too low, this will encourage spider mite. It is usually sufficient to spray the plant daily with cold water to prevent this happening. If you regularly prune it, it will gradually develop into a bushy plant which will flower profusely. As soon as the buds become visible in spring, feed it some extra artificial fertilizer every two weeks. Repot the plant when it has flowered, and prune it at the same time.

The myrtle grows best in soil rich in humus, composed, for example, of equal parts of peat, potting compost and well-rotted manure. Although it can be grown from seed, it is easier to propagate by taking cuttings. Choose tops which are not too woody, 5–7cm long, and encourage roots to form by placing them in a covered pot of peat with some rooting powder. Pot the cuttings in separate pots after 4–6 weeks.

Polyanthus Narcissus

Scientific name: Narcissus tazetta L.
Family name: Amaryllidaceae
Natural habitat: Mediterranean area
English name: Polyanthus narcissus
Biblical name: crocus

The desert and the parched land will be glad; the wilderness will rejoice and blossom. Like the crocus, it will burst into bloom; it will rejoice greatly and shout for joy.

ISAIAH 35:1–2

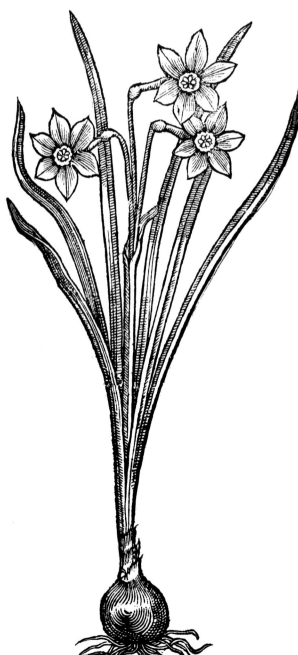

It feels as though spring has only really arrived when the first bulbs start to bloom. Beginning with winter aconites, snowdrops and crocuses, soon followed by narcissi, tulips and hyacinths, nature revives again after the cold, dark winter.

This feeling is not only common in northern countries, but is also experienced in warmer zones. Following a long period of drought, there is usually quite a lot of rainfall in these regions during the winter months. As soon as the temperature rises, plants come back to life, only to be quickly shrivelled up again in the fierce sunlight. Plants which grow from bulbs and tubers are particularly tolerant of such extreme fluctuations of temperature. The part of the plant which is underground, often insulated by a layer of stones, will continue to grow every year.

To enjoy masses of narcissi, we do not even have to go to the Holy Land. In the Pyrenees, for example, there are also large numbers of narcissi. Often there are so many that when they are blooming, the air is almost saturated with the characteristic heavy, sweet odour. Narcissi also grow abundantly in the plain of Sharon, the fertile strip of land between the mountains in the central part of the Holy Land, and in the valleys surrounding Jerusalem, Jericho, Beirut, and Sidon. This is the multi-headed polyanthus narcissus. In areas where it grows wild, the flowers are picked in large numbers, and you will find a bunch of these fragrant narcissi in virtually every living-room.

The name of the genus *Narcissus* is derived from Narkissos, a son of the river god, Kephissos, and the nymph, Leiriope. According to Greek mythology, he was a handsome young man, and many women fell in love with him, but he remained unmoved by their charms. One of his admirers, the nymph Echo, who was also unable to seduce him, turned to Nemesis or Fate— or in some versions of the story to Aphrodite, the goddess of love—seeking revenge. The goddess heard her prayer, and when Narkissos, exhausted from hunting, went to quench his thirst in a stream, he saw his reflection, which he did not recognize, and immediately fell in love with it. He could not stop staring at himself in the water, and eventually he completely pined away. Then the vengeful goddess took pity on him and changed him into a white flower with a yellow heart.

Many poets wrote about Narkissos' fate, so Linnaeus called the plant *Narcissus poeticus L.,* the poet's narcissus. A sub-species of this narcissus, with white petals and a yellow heart, is found on the Balkan peninsula.

The name 'narcissus' is sometimes linked to the Greek word *narke*, an anaesthetic or narcotic, referring to the strong fragrance of some varieties of these flowers. In the Negev desert and in the vicinity of

Mount Carmel, hundreds of thousands of narcissus bulbs are grown for export, particularly of the *papyraceus* variety. These find their way all over the world, as the well-known 'Paperwhite' narcissus, with the brand name 'Carmel'.

GROWING TIPS
If you plant the bulbs several weeks before Christmas in a bowl of gravel and water, they will flower at Christmas. As they are not frost hardy, they can only be grown indoors. When the bulbs have finished flowering, they can be thrown away.

In warm regions where there is no frost, these narcissi are propagated by means of clisters.

NARCISSUS JONQUILA, indigenous to Southern Europe and North Africa, is also suitable for growing in pots.

White Watercress

Scientific name: Nasturtium officinale R.Br
Family name: Cruciferae
Natural habitat: Europe
English name: watercress
Biblical name: bitter herbs

---

*They are to eat the lamb, together with unleavened bread and
bitter herbs.*

NUMBERS 9:11

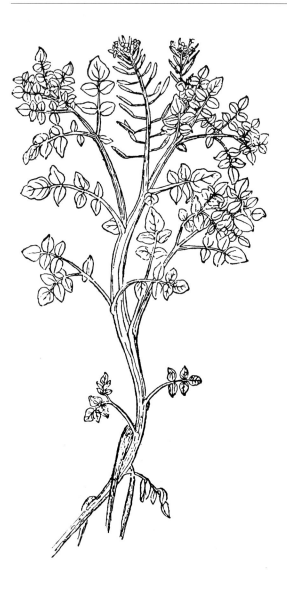

In Bible times, some vegetables which are extremely
common now, such as endive and lettuce, were classed
as 'bitter herbs'. Over the years the bitter taste of these
vegetables has almost entirely disappeared, through a
process of breeding and selection. However, the
original taste of watercress *(Nasturtium officinale)*, which
has an important place in the group of bitter herbs, has
not changed very much.

The genus *Nasturtium* consists of about six different
varieties, and belongs to the family Cruciferae.
Nasturtium officinale is a perennial plant which grows new
shoots several times a season after it has been cut. In the
Holy Land, watercress grows wild along the banks of
streams and rivers. The inhabitants collect the young
stems with their many tender leaves, which are
considered a delicacy. In other countries too, the plant
can be found wild in watery spots though it is quite
rare.

Since the eleventh century, watercress (French:
cresson; German: *kresse;* Dutch: *waterkers)* has been
cultivated for consumption on an ever-larger scale,
especially in southern Europe. The taste is sharp rather
than bitter, and is so much appreciated nowadays that
most greengrocers sell it. It is usually eaten raw in
salads, or as a garnish with *hors d'oeuvres.*

GROWING TIPS

If you have running water in your garden you can grow
watercress quite easily. Once it has been sown, the plant
will survive for years.

It is also possible to grow watercress in a watertight
container. The roots should always be submerged
several centimetres underwater, and it is important to
change the water regularly.

Oleander

Scientific name: Nerium oleander L.
Family name: Apocynaceae
Natural habitat: Mediterranean area
English name: oleander
Biblical name: rose

---

*Listen to me, devout children, and blossom like the rose that
grows on the bank of a watercourse.*
ECCLESIASTICUS 39:14

NERIUM OLEANDER

According to some, the 'rose that grows on the bank of a watercourse' in the above passage refers to a variety of willow, but others believe that this must be a reference to the oleander *(Nerium oleander)*. This difference of opinion could have arisen simply because, except when they are flowering, oleander bushes look very similar to willows from a distance. As far as we can ascertain, the oleander is only mentioned in the Deuterocanonical books (part of the Apocrypha).

The evergreen oleander grows to a height of about 3m, and is common in countries around the Mediterranean. Like the willow, it does best along riverbanks. It is often found growing in an apparently dry river bed, where it can find enough water some way down to develop fully. In the Holy Land, oleanders grow abundantly along the banks of the River Jordan, the Sea of Galilee, the Lake of Tiberias, in Samaria, and around the Dead Sea, as well as along small streams and near wells.

This woody plant belongs to the periwinkle family (Apocynaceae), and most of us are familiar with it. It is a welcome reminder of holidays in the Mediterranean area. As the oleander does so well in gardens in those regions, many varieties have been developed by a process of breeding and selection to make the most of the fragrant flowers growing in bunches at the end of the stems. There are varieties with pink, white, red, and even yellow flowers, varying in diameter between 2 and 5cm, sometimes growing as single and sometimes as double flowers. The leathery leaves grow in groups of three. They are long and thin, with little variation in the colouring.

In their natural habitat, oleanders form long, double cylindrical fruits. The hairy seeds, released at the end of the summer when the fruits burst open, are scattered by the wind.

Every part of this plant, particularly the colourless juice released when a leaf breaks off or a stem is cut, is extremely poisonous, so take care when pruning, for example, not to get any of the juice in a wound, or in your mouth or eyes.

GROWING TIPS

It is best to propagate the oleander by taking cuttings. You will be far more successful with cuttings from beautiful specimens which flower profusely. A length of about 15cm, of a top cutting or one from lower down, is enough for this. The cuttings will take root in summer in a glass of water or a pot of moist peat without any rooting powder. Once the roots have formed, the young plants can be potted in 5cm pots.

They will develop very well in a soil rich in nutrients, consisting of equal parts of peat, well-rotted manure, and soil. During the growing period make sure that you water the plants frequently and feed them with artificial fertilizer every two weeks. It is a good idea to place the oleander plants outside in the garden or on a balcony, in a warm, sunny spot, during the summer and early autumn. Provided they always have enough water and are fed regularly, they will flower profusely.

Repot the plants regularly to stimulate growth. Plants which have grown too large can be pruned back hard in the autumn without any ill effects.

It is best if the plant is kept in a cool place ($5°$ C) during the winter. As long as the earth is kept fairly dry, the oleander does not have any special requirements as regards light. In the spring it can be repotted or put in a new tub again. If the air is too dry and too warm, you may get infestations of scale insects, cottony maple scale, woolly aphids, and red spider mite. This can be prevented by regularly spraying the whole plant with cold water. Scale insects can be removed using cotton wool soaked in methylated spirits. Repeat this about three times at intervals of a fortnight, to prevent any surviving insects from reproducing.

Notobasis

Scientific name: Notobasis syriaca (L.) Cass.
Family name: Compositae
Natural habitat: Mediterranean area
English name: Notobasis
Biblical name: thorn

Other seed fell among thorns, which grew up and choked the plants.

MATTHEW 13:7

Notobasis syriaca belongs to the Compositae family and was very common even in Bible times, when, together with other varieties of thistles, it grew along the edges of cornfields, choking the young grain. This is the variety of thorn referred to in the parable of the seed and the sower.

Like some of the other tall thistles, this could also have been the variety mentioned in the following passage from Judges 8:16. 'He took the elders of the town and taught the men of Succoth a lesson by punishing them with desert thorns and briers.' *Notobasis*, which can sometimes grow to a height of 1m, may well have been the thorn used for this beating, particularly as local people know that it is very common in Ofra, the home of Gideon.

It is an annual, and sometimes a biennial thistle, which grows to a height of over 60cm. The leaves are leathery with sharp thorns; they are a marbled white with silvery white veins and more or less wrap round the stem. The flowers are arranged in groups together. They are purple and are surrounded by long, enveloping leaves with sharp thorns. At the end of the season when the flowers have ripened, the small seeds, which resemble sunflower seeds, pop out, each at the end of a long, silvery-white parachute-like filament. The seed is then dispersed by the wind.

GROWING TIPS

Like the Our Lady's thistle *(Silybum marianum)*, *Notobasis syriaca* can also be cultivated as a biennial plant. In this case, the seed should be sown in the late summer. You will have larger plants the following year and they will flower more profusely. However, the disadvantage is that in wet or very severe winters, the young plants may freeze.

To be sure that the plants will flower, you should sow them in spring rather than autumn. The best time to do this is at the end of spring, or even early summer. As *Notobasis* plants have strongly developed tap roots and are therefore difficult to transplant, sow the seeds some distance apart (approximately 15–20cm). If the plants are still too close together when they come up, they can easily be thinned out.

In contrast with the conditions in their country of origin—dry fields in Mediterranean areas—the plants will grow into large specimens in cooler climates if the soil is fertile and there is a lot of rain, and they will easily exceed the usual height of approximately 60cm. You will usually have to support the long stems at an early stage.

Waterlily

Scientific name: Nymphaea lotus L.
Family name: Nymphaeaceae
Natural habitat: Egypt
English name: waterlily
Biblical name: lily

The capitals on top of the pillars in the portico were in the shape of lilies, four cubits high.

1 KINGS 7:19

Although some people assume that the capitals in the text quoted above were decorated with the flowers of the Madonna lily *(Lilium candidum)*, the use of waterlilies—also referred to as 'lotus' or 'lotus plants' (Job 40:16-17)—should certainly not be excluded as the possible ornamentation.

Long before the birth of Christ, waterlilies grew abundantly in the Nile Basin, where they were known as 'lotus flowers.' The sacred lotus *(Nelumbo nucifera)*, described by Herodotus (484–424 BC), must have been introduced into Egypt shortly before his time. This can be deduced from the fact that *Nelumbo nucifera*, which originates from the Far East, was not depicted on Egyptian murals before that time, and from the fact that the striking pea-sized seeds, which were a common source of food, have never been found in excavations dating from the time before Herodotus. For these reasons, it may therefore be assumed that the lilies which were used as the example for ornamentation in earlier periods must have been two indigenous varieties: the white flowering tropical waterlily, also known as the white lotus, *Nymphaea lotus,* and the blue lotus, *Nymphaea coerulea.* The rosette-shaped flowers of the waterlily which decorated the pillars of Solomon's temple, according to the Old Testament, and similar pictures in earlier Egyptian tombs, can therefore probably be traced back to these indigenous varieties.

Far less spectacular than the two tropical varieties mentioned above, is the ordinary waterlily, *Nymphaea alba,* which grows not only in the Holy Land, but is also fairly common elsewhere in Europe. At the end of the 19th century, many varieties were developed through cross-breeding, particularly by the French waterlily specialist, Marliac. These have different sizes and colours and are used to enhance large and small ponds and lakes.

GROWING TIPS

Waterlilies can only be grown in ponds. They do not have to be very large. A pond with a diameter of 1m and a depth of 30cm is big enough for growing a waterlily as long as you choose a small variety. As a rule, well-stocked garden centres and nurseries specializing in water plants will have a wide range of large and small waterlily hybrids in stock. In rather larger ponds, you will have to use a basket filled with mud in which the waterlily is planted, in order to prevent the plant from floating away, and to counteract the current. Place this on the bed and the roots will soon become anchored in the ground. In shallow ponds the plant can be directly planted in the mud. Then place some support around the heart of the plant to prevent drifting.

NYMPHAEA LOTUS

Olive

Scientific name: Olea europaea L.
Family name: Oleaceae
Natural habitat: Mediterranean area
English name: olive
Biblical name: olive

He waited seven more days and again sent out the dove from the ark. When the dove returned to him in the evening, there in its beak was a freshly plucked olive leaf!
GENESIS 8:10–11

The olive, *Olea europaea*, still grows abundantly in the Holy Land. In many places it is the only tree of any kind to be seen in the landscape, and virtually no other tree has played such an important role in the history of human civilization.

It is assumed that *Olea europaea* originated in western Asia, and not in southern Europe, as its name would suggest. Four different varieties can be found in the Holy Land. The branches of the wild variety (not to be confused with the wild olive or oleaster, of the genus *Elaeagnus*), which has not been selectively bred, have a compact, rigid shape, and numerous thorns. The cultivated varieties are decorative, with many branches (Hosea 14:7). They can grow to a height of 7m or more, and have a gnarled trunk covered in ash-grey bark. The leathery-green leaves are oval, long or lanciform, and in some cases can even be almost circular, with slightly furled edges and a felty grey underside. The small white or yellow flowers grow in bunches in the axilla of the leaves. In general, they are fertilized by the wind, but in some cases fertilization takes place by bees or other insects.

The fruits are fairly large, oval in shape, and black or dark blue/violet in colour. They grow to a length of about 4cm and are 3cm thick, but the shape varies, depending on the variety, between round, oval, blunt and pointed. Only a small number of the flowers form fruit; usually 50 per cent fall off, while of the rest only 10–20 per cent grow into ripe olives.

Although olives are very bitter, they can be eaten raw, ripe or unripe. Usually they are preserved in a brine solution. The valuable olive oil is extracted from the fleshy, outer part of the fruit, but the seed kernel also contains oil. In Bible times the oil was extracted by pressing the fruit with a vertical, round millstone. One crop from a mature tree produces approximately 500kg oil.

For a tree to produce good fruit, it must be grafted. For this purpose, a twig of a highly productive specimen is grafted onto a sturdy, rapidly growing trunk. Trees which have not been grafted produce only poor fruit. This explains the powerful symbolic message in chapter 11 of Paul's letter to the Romans.

The olives are harvested in late autumn or during the winter months. This is done simply by shaking the branches of the tree or beating them with sticks. A few fruits were always left on the largest branches for the poor, and for 'strangers, orphans and widows' who collected them after the harvest. One tree could easily provide a whole family with the oil they needed.

However, an olive tree does require some care. If the tree is not looked after, it will bear hardly any fruit, as can be seen in trees on abandoned plantations.

The hard, fine-grained wood of the trunk and branches is a bright yellow or amber colour, with reddish irregular veins giving it a beautifully grained appearance. Nowadays olive wood is still highly prized because many valuable articles can be made from it.

The olive tree grows extremely slowly and may grow to a great age. Some of the trees on the Mount of Olives and in the Garden of Gethsemane where Jesus spent his last night of liberty are said to have been there since the birth of Christ, but this is unlikely, because historians of that time relate how the Roman emperor Vespasian had all the olive trees cut down. However, it is not easy to kill off an olive tree without digging up its roots. Trees which are sawn down always form new shoots in different places, and in most cases eventually grow several new trunks.

In ancient times, the cultivation of olive trees was so widespread and commonplace that the olive groves in the Bible are mentioned almost in one breath with vineyards and cornfields. Virtually every village had its own olive plantation or grove. Because of its purity, olive oil was used in coronations and to anoint high priests and other important officials. The oil was also used during sacrifices, as fuel for lamps, and to strengthen hair and skin. In addition, medicinal properties were ascribed to it, and it was used as a base for the perfumed ointments which were sold in ancient Rome and Athens.

In the gardens described in the Bible, the olive often appears to have an important place. The 'gardens' in the Middle East at that time did not have as many flowers as you might imagine. In general, they were orchards—surrounded by thorny hedges or walls— mainly of olive trees, with possibly a fig tree here and there. Kings and their wealthy subjects would also have almond, walnut, pistachio and other trees, and various herbs. There was usually a tower in every orchard, from which the guard would make sure that wild animals or thieves stayed at a distance.

is said to have sat thinking about original sin at the foot of this tree with three trunks. Solomon is supposed to have cut down the tree, but its wood could not be used. It was thrown into a marsh, where it floated and served as a bridge for the Queen of Sheba. Eventually, the wood was used for the cross on which Jesus was crucified.

GROWING TIPS

Olea europaea makes an excellent pot plant. This is because the rather tough leathery leaves lose very little water through evaporation, so the plant is suited by the rather dry indoor atmosphere. To grow an olive indoors successfully, it is essential to place the plant in a light and preferably sunny spot. During the period of growth, which lasts from late spring to autumn, the earth in the pot should normally be kept moist, and some artificial fertilizer can be added to the water once a month during watering, to stimulate growth.

In winter, when the olive virtually stops growing because of the lack of light, the soil in the pot should be kept rather dry. During the winter, place it in a cool room with a temperature of approximately 5° C If this is not possible, it will also be necessary to water the plant more during the winter months, as it will lose more water through evaporation in a warm room.

You can cultivate the olive very easily outside during the summer months. It can be moved outdoors from early summer to the end of autumn. During these months, a sunny spot in the garden will ensure that the plant will revive quickly after the winter. It is best to repot the plant in spring, when it starts to form new shoots. Use soil rich in nutrients, rather than soil with a light composition. You will get good results with a mixture of one part potting compost and one part peat. Both the leaves and the new twigs are sometimes attacked by scale insects and cottony maple scale. It is difficult to combat these indoors, but the best way to do this is by removing them with cotton wool soaked in methylated spirits. Do this regularly to prevent the young scale insects from reproducing.

These eastern 'gardens' were described by travellers as groups of trees planted in a disorderly fashion, without any paths, attractive nooks and crannies or anything to recommend them, from the point of view of garden design. Gethsemane was such an olive grove garden, at the foot of the Mount of Olives, where there were also some oil presses. They primarily served a practical purpose, as places where fruit and herbs were grown, and where you could find shade.

The oldest reference in the Bible to the olive must be that in the story of the Flood, when the dove returned to Noah with an olive leaf in its beak as proof that the waters God had sent in anger had gone down. Since that time, both the dove and the olive branch have become universal symbols of peace and friendship.

In the Orient, the olive is also the symbol of prosperity, divine blessing, beauty, wealth, and strength. In Greek and Roman mythology, the olive was the symbol of the goddess Athena or Minerva, the goddess of wisdom. She was said to have given the olive to the human race, and in gratitude they named the city of Athens after her. In Italy, an olive twig is sometimes still hung over the door of a house, to keep the devil, witches and evil spirits at bay.

Numerous legends arose about the olive, particularly during the Middle Ages. For example, it was said that the seeds of the olive tree, the cypress and the cedar were given to Seth, Adam's son, by the angel who guarded the Garden of Eden, when his father was dying. Planted in Adam's mouth, they grew into a tree with three trunks: one of the olive tree, one of the cypress and one of the cedar.

The legend continues with the story of David, who

Ornithogalum

Scientific name: Ornithogalum narbonense L.
Family name: Liliaceae
Natural habitat: southern Europe
English name: ornithogalum, star of Bethlehem
Biblical name: dove's dung

Some time later, Ben-hadad, King of Aram, mobilised his entire army and marched up and laid siege to Samaria. There was a great famine in the city; the siege lasted so long that a donkey's head sold for eighty shekels of silver, and a fourth of a cab of dove's dung for five shekels.

2 KINGS 6:24–25

The reference to dove's dung in this passage is generally translated as 'seed pods' nowadays. However, it could also refer to an *Ornithogalum*. A number of different varieties of *Ornithogalum* grow wild in the Mediterranean area. In the spring they flower profusely, and do look rather like dove's excrement. The Bible reference is to the bulbs of the plant being used as food in times of poverty, when there was nothing else to eat, and when a quarter measure was worth five pieces of silver.

As most of the plants of this genus are poisonous, it is fairly certain that the type referred to here is *Ornithogalum narbonense*, which is edible. The Latin name of the genus *Ornithogalum*, derived from the Greek name of the plant *ornithogalon* (*ornithos*, 'bird', and *gala*, 'milk'), was given by Linnaeus to this genus, because he assumed that this was the plant described in the Bible as 'dove's dung'.

Nowadays, about 150 different varieties can be distinguished, which can all be found in Europe. One of these, *Ornithogalum umbellatum*, the well-known star of Bethlehem, is among the indigenous flora of more northerly parts of Europe, though it is fairly rare. You are most likely to find the plant in grassland or in wet, deciduous woodland, particularly near dunes. Moreover, these are usually specimens which are growing wild, but originated from bulb growers or gardens. It is an attractive plant which flowers easily, and the bulbs are not expensive to buy in autumn. Other varieties which are also available in autumn, though they are less common, are *Ornithogalum nutans* (drooping star-of-Bethlehem), which grows to a height of about 30–50cm and has greenish-white hanging flowers, and *Ornithogalum pyramidale*, which grows to about 40–70cm high in a pyramid, with large numbers of star-shaped flowers. In spring, you can also buy the bulbs of *Ornithogalum thyrsoides*, which is widely cultivated for cut flowers, and *Ornithogalum arabicum*. These two varieties are frost-tender, and must therefore be dug up and stored in frost-free conditions in winter.

GROWING TIPS

All the varieties of *Ornithogalum* which are winter hardy should be planted in autumn. Although they particularly thrive in slightly shaded spots, they can also flourish in full sunlight. The plant has no requirements as regards the composition of the soil. The star of Bethlehem likes to grow unchecked. As the years pass, it grows back more profusely every year. Before the plant flowers in early summer, there is a lot of leaf growth. This may be a disadvantage for planting in small gardens, as this large quantity of green, both before and after the flowering period, is not so attractive.

Varieties which are not hardy in winter should be planted in early summer. Choose a sunny spot in the garden with soil that is rich in nutrients. All varieties of *Ornithogalum* are easy to propagate either from seed, or from the many small bulbs which develop around the original bulb.

ORNITHOGALUM UMBELLATUM

Christ's Thorn

Scientific name: Paliurus spina-christi Miller
Family name: Rhamnaceae
Natural habitat: Mediterranean area, the Balkan
                       peninsula and the Black Sea
English name: Christ's thorn
Biblical name: thornbush

*Instead of the thornbush will grow the pine tree, and instead of
briers the myrtle will grow. This will be for the Lord's renown,
for an everlasting sign, which will not be destroyed.*

ISAIAH 55:13

As we see time and again, it is extremely difficult to be
quite certain which particular plant is meant from
references to plants in the Bible. The English names of
Christ's thorn or crown of thorns is linked with several
different plants.

Undoubtedly one of the best known 'crown of
thorns' is a popular pot plant, *Euphorbia milii*, but this
plant is not related to the real Christ's thorn in any way.
It belongs to the family Euphorbiaceae, was originally
indigenous to Madagascar, and was certainly not
known in the Holy Land at the time of Christ.

Gleditsia triacanthos, the honey locust, has also been
called Christ's thorn. This woody plant grows wild in
the northeast and central parts of the United States,
and is also completely hardy in winter in northern
Europe. It grows into an enormous tree, which can
reach a height of over 15m. It owes its popular name to
the fact that not only are its branches covered with
thorns, but when it is mature, the trunk also has many
thorns, generally grouped together.

The reality is that the Bible writers use the term
'thorn' to refer to a number of thorny plants. The
thorns in Isaiah 7:19 and 55:13 and in Matthew 7:16
are believed to be those of *Zizyphus spina-christi,* also
known as Christ's thorn. However, it is unlikely to have
been the plant really used for the crown of thorns,
because it can grow into a large tree, over 10m tall.

Therefore it is more likely that to make Christ's
crown of thorns, twigs were picked from the shrub
Paliurus spina-christi, which grows everywhere along the
roads of the Holy Land, and is between 1 and 3m tall.

This plant, a member of the Rhamnaceae family,
was originally found in areas from southern Europe as
far as China. In 1594, Clusius brought it to the

Netherlands. This Christ's thorn is not completely hardy in winter in the cooler climate, but like many plants of this type from Mediterranean areas, older specimens are more resistant to the cold than younger ones. Some older shrubs have been known to survive fairly severe winters with temperatures of ¯20° C

GROWING TIPS
If you plant it in a warm, sunny spot in rich, well-drained soil, *Paliurus spina-christi* will develop into an attractive shrub between 1 and 2m tall. It will flower in mid- to late summer. During this time it is a light yellow colour because of its hundreds of small flowers. These will rarely develop their striking fruit in cooler areas, as the growing season is usually too short—rather a pity, for the fruit is very distinctive.

It is easiest to propagate *Paliurus spina-christi* from seed. You can also take cuttings, but the plant does not form roots very easily, and must be encouraged with the help of warm soil and rooting powder.

PALIURUS SPINA-CHRISTI

Millet

Scientific name: Panicum miliaceum L.
Family name: Gramineae
Natural habitat: central, southern and eastern
    Europe, China and Central Asia
English name: millet
Biblical name: millet

Take wheat and barley, beans and lentils, millet and spelt; put them into a container and make them into a bread for yourself.

EZEKIEL 4:9

Millet *(Panicum)* and guinea corn *(sorghum)* are grown in many different varieties in tropical and sub-tropical areas throughout the world, as intensively as different grains are grown in temperate climates. They belong to the annual grass plants (Gramineae), and are very similar to corn as regards their shape and growth. When they are grown in temperate conditions, the plants generally develop very well, though they do not form great quantities of seed, due to the lack of warmth. In fact, that is the reason why these plants are not more generally grown in Northern Europe.

Depending on the variety, sorghum grows to a height of 1–3m, while millet is shorter. Unlike corn, these plants thrive in less fertile and drier soil. They are not only an extremely important source of food for human consumption, but are also important for cattle food. The seed plumes of sorghum particularly grow to enormous lengths. Often they are so large that a mature plume will provide a whole meal for a family of four or five.

Because of its spectacular appearance, these long plumes are often used in bouquets of dried flowers. The same also applies for the plumes of millet, which are more graceful, but not so large. Usually only the seed plumes are harvested, and the rest of the plant is left to die away on the land. After a while, wind and weather leave only long, bare stalks, which may be used for roofing, for building enclosures, and as fuel.

GROWING TIPS

In cooler climates, millet *(Panicum miliaceum)* and guinea corn *(Sorghum bicolor)* are fairly easy to grow, especially during warm summers.

Sow the seed in a sunny spot at the beginning of summer, and the plants will grow to a height of 1–1.5m. It is time to harvest them as soon as the leaves turn a brownish colour. If you leave the plumes on the plants too long, birds will peck out all the seeds.

The plumes, which can be used to make attractive bouquets of dried flowers with other ornamental grasses, should be cut off so that the stalks are as long as possible. Then hang them up to dry in a well-ventilated, shady spot, upside down, in not too large bunches.

Guinea corn *(Sorghum bicolor)* needs to be treated in a similar way. If you want to be able to harvest beautiful, well-formed seed plumes before the first frost, it is a good idea to start the seedlings off indoors in spring. They can then be planted outside in a warm and sunny spot at the beginning of summer.

They may grow so quickly that within a few months they reach a height of 2 or even 3m. At the end of the summer, plumes, which sometimes reach enormous proportions, develop on the longest stems. As long as the frosts are not too early, these can be harvested when they are more or less ripe, at the end of the autumn. They can be used in the same way as millet for making arrangements of dried flowers.

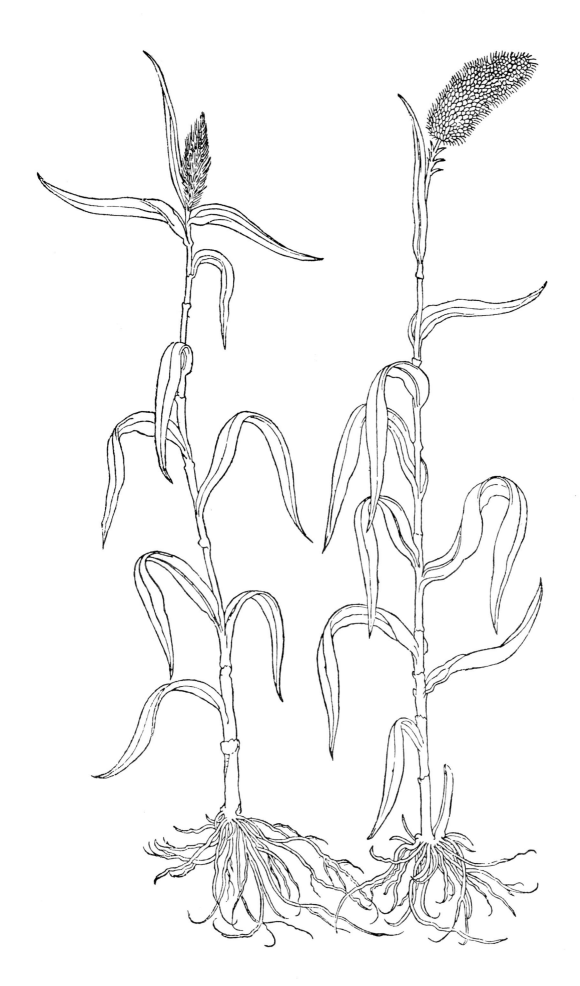

Poppy

Scientific name: Papaver rhoeas L.
Family name: Papaveraceae
Natural habitat: Asia, Europe
English name: poppy
Biblical name: flower of the field

All men are like grass, and all their glory is like the flowers of the field. The grass withers and the flowers fall, because the breath of the Lord blows on them. Surely the people are grass. The grass withers and the flowers fall, but the word of our God stands for ever.

ISAIAH 40:6–8

The poppy *(Papaver rhoeas)* not only grows profusely in the Holy Land and other Mediterranean areas, but is also a common sight in more temperate regions. In the past, before the use of chemical herbicides and insecticides, this annual plant was a common sight in wheatfields. Nowadays, these beautiful red flowers are found mainly on freshly cleared building sites and roadside verges—wherever the soil has been freshly turned.

Unfortunately, the season in which this plant brightens up the whole area with its bright red flowers waving in the wind is very short. It is all over after about three weeks, and then only the seed heads remain to remind us of the exuberance of their flowering. As other perennial weeds take over the areas where poppies grow and competition becomes too great, this annual plant is now fighting for survival.

It is different in the arid fields of Mediterranean

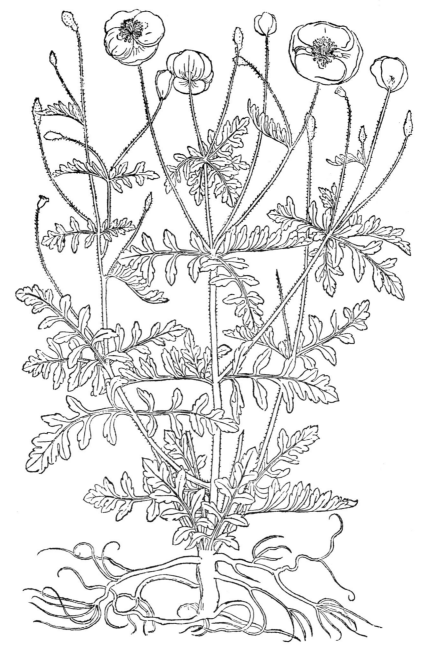

PAPAVER RHOEAS

lands, which are regularly ploughed, for this stimulates the growth and flowering of *Papaver rhoeas*. Poppy seeds are still able to germinate after they have been in the earth for a long time. When conditions become favourable, for example, after a field is ploughed, new plants appear immediately. The flowers do not contain any nectar but produce large quantities of pollen, which is dispersed by insects.

GROWING TIPS
It is because of the poppy's exuberant growth that over the centuries a large variety of hybrids with a great diversity of colours and sizes have been bred through a process of selection. For keen gardeners, the large

double varieties of *Papaver somniferum* are particularly attractive, although the cultivated varieties of *Papaver rhoeas* with smaller flowers should by no means be forgotten.

It is an extremely easy plant to grow and has absolutely no requirements as regards the composition of the soil. Sown in the open ground in spring, the plants will start flowering profusely a few months later. If you sow at regular intervals of, for example, three weeks, until mid summer, it is possible to have flowers in bloom until mid autumn. When the ripe seedheads have been dried, they can be used in arrangements of dried flowers.

Date Palm

Scientific name: Phoenix dactylifera L.
Family name: Palmae
Natural habitat: southern Europe, northern Africa
                       and southwest Asia
English name: date palm
Biblical name: palm

---

*The next day the great crowd that had come for the Feast heard
that Jesus was on his way to Jerusalem. They took palm branches
and went out to meet him . . .*

JOHN 12:12–13

There is absolutely no doubt that the palm which is
frequently mentioned in the Bible is the date palm
Phoenix dactylifera. In Bible times, this palm was very
common both in the Holy Land and in Egypt.

Mature specimens, which can reach a height of
more than 25m, are a characteristic feature of the
landscape, particularly when there are several growing
close together. The typical oasis generally consists of
small or large groups of date palms. In some areas they

grow in broad river valleys, though they also grow on
their own in the middle of the land where they often
serve as landmarks for passing caravans.

The date palm is found over a wide area, stretching
from India to Western Asia, and from Arabia, Sinai
and Egypt to other North African countries.
Nowadays, the date palm is also grown on a large scale
for its fruit in California and Spain.

The genus *Phoenix,* and therefore also the date
palm, is deciduous. The small, light yellow, leathery
flowers are bunched together in a large spadix, which
generally hangs down and can grow to a length of 75–
100cm. The male flowers consist of a triple calyx and a
three-leafed corolla, and have six stamens. The female
flowers have six stem-shaped, false stamens, and three
ovaries. One of these develops into a long fruit the size
of a plum, which is orange-brown or black in colour.
The bunches of fruit which develop in this way can
weigh up to 10–15kg, depending on type. Each tree
can produce 50–100kg per year, and often even more.
The fruit (dates) ripen in about five months. A warm
climate (40°C or more) and sufficient moisture for the
roots are essential conditions for good fruit
production.

When the tree flowers, it can be artificially
fertilized by hanging bunches of male flowers in female
trees. This method has successfully been used from
ancient times.

PHOENIX DACTYLIFERA

Since date palms have been cultivated, many types have been bred for high yields of fruit. Although they are easy to grow from seed, these highly productive plants are usually propagated from runners which already start bearing fruit after five or six years. However, the date palm, which can have a lifespan of two hundred years, only produces its maximum yield after about thirty years.

Like other plants mentioned in the Bible, the date palm was often used as a motif in architecture, and the leaves, bunches of fruit, and characteristically shaped trunk were all depicted. The large springy leaves curving outwards together form an enormous crown, and can reach a length of approximately 3m. In the Bible, they are called palm branches, and were used particularly during festive celebrations. This ancient custom survives today on Palm Sunday. The long leaves are still used as roofing material, for fencing, and for plaiting mats, baskets and hats. The fibrous 'wood' is also used for building.

However, the date palm is particularly important to local people because of the high nutritional value of the fruit. In addition, dates are an important product for export. The large, hard stones are often soaked or ground to make cattle food, or roasted, ground and used as surrogate coffee. When they are blooming, the enormous bunches of flowers produce large quantities of honey, which is carefully collected and fermented to make a sweet alcoholic beverage, rather like a liqueur. Another alcoholic beverage is made from fermented ripe fruit.

GROWING TIPS

Date palms are very easy to grow from seed in cooler climates as well. The stones of candied dates will germinate after about one year if they are sown in moist peat which is constantly kept damp and warm. When the only seed leaf of this monocotyledonous plant is about 10 cm long, the young date palm is potted in a fairly deep pot, so that the long taproot can continue to grow undisturbed. It is best to use soil rich in nutrients to stimulate growth, composed of one part of peat to one part of soil and one part of old, well-rotted stable manure.

Even if you treat the seedling with care, and place it in a warm spot on the windowsill, it will only develop slowly. It will take about ten years for a fair-sized plant to develop. Obviously it will have to be repotted regularly during this time, and the plant should always be placed in a very light and preferably sunny spot.

Take great care to ensure that the leaves are not attacked by red spider mite. This tiny little spider, which can develop in large numbers, especially in dry sunny conditions, can make short work of the plant very quickly. Such an infestation can only be treated at that stage with highly toxic remedies which are not suitable for use in the living-room. A very easy way of preventing infestations of red spider mite is to place the whole plant under a cold shower regularly. Red spider mites hate the cold and will simply disappear as a result of this treatment.

The Canary date palm, originating from the Canary Islands, is closely related to the date palm and extremely popular as a pot plant. The beautiful ochre-coloured fruit is inedible, but it is used at Christmas for ornamental purposes. Young and healthy specimens are available everywhere at little cost as pot plants. The Canary date palm will also be attacked by the dreaded red spider mite within a short time in warm, dry conditions. In order to get the best out of any *Phoenix*, it is therefore best to place it in a light and preferably sunny spot which is not too warm.

During the summer months you can move the plant outdoors to a warm, sunny spot. For plants which are not directly accustomed to bright sunlight, it is a good idea to let them get used to it gradually by covering them with a piece of net curtain. This prevents the leaves from being burnt. You should also regularly feed the plant with artificial fertilizer, particularly during the growing season. During the summer months, always make sure that the earth in the pot is kept moist.

Umbrella Pine

Scientific name: Pinus pinea L.
Family name: Pinaceae
Natural habitat: Mediterranean area
English name: umbrella pine
Biblical name: pine

The glory of Lebanon will come to you, the pine, the fir and the cypress together, to adorn the place of my sanctuary . . .
ISAIAH 60:13

Although there is still some difference of opinion about the identity of the conifers which are often mentioned in the Bible, it can be stated with absolute certainty that the umbrella pine *(Pinus pinea)* could be found in the Holy Land in large numbers then, as it is now.

The large cones of this pine tree contain many nutty, wingless seeds up to 2cm long. When the thick, hard shell is removed, a white kernel is found inside which contains a great deal of oil and has a pleasant taste. Peeled seeds are a delicacy, used to garnish cakes, tarts, and biscuits. For this reason, the nuts are eagerly collected by children wherever the umbrella pine grows.

In Mediterranean countries the umbrella pine has a strong impact on the appearance of the landscape because of its striking and extremely characteristic shape. A mature tree has a remarkable umbrella-shaped crown at the end of a trunk which is usually straight and can grow up to 15–25m tall. Nearer the coast, the trunk is often shorter and crooked, and in windy spots it can be distorted into bizarre shapes.

The pine needles grow in pairs and are about 10–15cm long. They are fairly coarse with sharp ends. The cones have virtually no stem. They grow singly or sometimes in pairs, and are pressed closely against the branches. It is only after three years when they have grown out completely that they open up and the seeds between the thick scales are released. The empty cones often fall off the tree after a storm, and are collected and used as fuel.

GROWING TIPS

The umbrella pine is slightly frost tender, but can survive the winter out of doors, provided that it is planted in a warm and protected spot in well-drained soil, and that it is not too young a specimen. It can also be grown very well in a tub if it spends the winter in a cool, light spot, free of frost. Move it outdoors during the summer months. Keep the roots fairly moist during this time and feed the plant with some extra fertilizer once a month. Keep the earth quite dry during the winter months, as the plant does not grow in this period and there is virtually no evaporation at a low temperature—approximately 5° C

You can grow *Pinus pinea* very easily from seed. Plant the seeds in a pot of moist peat placed on the windowsill. They will germinate fairly quickly, and the seedlings can then be repotted into individual pots. After several months, when the seedlings have grown sufficiently, repot them again.

When these seedlings are about one year old, they are sometimes sold as pot plants under the name *Pinus pinea* 'Silvercrest'. In contrast with mature plants, the needles of the seedlings are a beautiful bluish-grey colour.

PINUS PINEA

Mastic

Scientific name: Pistacia lentiscus L.
Family name: Pistaciaceae
Natural habitat: Mediterranean area, Portugal
English name: mastic
Biblical name: spice

---

*I have come into my garden, my sister, my bride; I have gathered
my myrrh with my spice.*
SONG OF SONGS 5:1

Pistacia lentiscus, the mastic tree, belongs to the Pistaciaceae family. Some of the members of the fairly small *Pistacia* genus are indigenous to Mediterranean areas, Afghanistan, Southeast Asia, and the southern part of the United States as far as Mexico and Guatemala.

The mastic tree is an evergreen, deciduous shrub which does not really deserve to be called a tree, as mature specimens do not grow taller than approximately 3m.

As a rule, the composite leaf consists of eight smaller leaves. These contain fragrant volatile oils which are emitted when the leaves are crushed.

The trunk and the thicker branches of *Pistacia lentiscus* contain resin which is released particularly when the bark is cut. It is a pale yellow colour, or sometimes slightly greenish, and has a pleasant odour and taste. The sap that drips from the trunk and branches, where they have been cut, sets as soon as it comes into contact with the outside air. It soon softens when it is chewed. This quality was discovered by people living in areas where the mastic tree grows wild, and the resin is often used as chewing gum.

Oil is pressed from the small, round, brownish-black root which the Arabians use for cooking and in loaves. Even in ancient times, the resin and oil of the mastic tree was used for embalming. The oil also played an important part in the preparation of mastic wine.

Finally, the resin provides a by no means insignificant raw material for the manufacture of various sorts of mastic, transparent varnishes and dyes.

GROWING TIPS

Like many woody plants, the mastic tree is frost tender. It can be cultivated in a container and moved to a sunny spot in the garden from early summer to the end of autumn. The earth in the pot should always be kept sufficiently moist. It is also important to feed the plant with extra fertilizer every month to stimulate growth. Prune the plant regularly, both to keep the shrub in shape and to prevent it from growing too large.

As the plant virtually stops growing during the winter months, it has little need of light and does not need much water. A cool room with a temperature of approximately 5°C is ideal.

Propagate the plant from seed or by taking cuttings. However, it is not easy to propagate the plant from a cutting, as it will only take root at a high temperature (approximately 30°C) and only with the help of a special rooting preparation.

Pistachio

Scientific name:	Pistacia vera L.
Family name:	Pistaciaceae
Natural habitat:	Iran to Central Asia
English name:	pistachio
Biblical name:	pistachio nut

Then their father Israel said to them, 'If it must be, then do this:
Put some of the best products of the land in your bags and take
them down to the man as a gift—a little balm and a little honey,
some spices and myrrh, some pistachio nuts and almonds.

GENESIS 43:11

Although the reference to pistachio nuts in Genesis 43:1 seems clear, the question once again arises about which tree bears these nuts. The nuts of *Pistacia terebinthus*, the true pistacia tree, are fairly small and have an extremely unpleasant taste, so it is more probable that the nuts referred to here are the much larger fruit of the closely related *Pistacia vera*. This relative of the pistacia tree produces the well-known delicious pistachio nuts, which were amongst the finest, most valuable commodities in Bible times, and were transported by caravans along the routes used at the time.

Originally *Pistacia vera* was indigenous to the dry regions of the plateaux in Afghanistan, the adjacent part of the Soviet Union, Iran and Turkey, where it grew to an average-sized tree about 7m in height. It is a member of the Pistaciaceae family, which comprises ten *Pistacia* varieties, and the pistachio nut is among a group of economically important food crops.

The nut itself is encased in a light woody shell, which opens on two sides. The soft kernel is a light yellow, slightly greenish colour, and the well-known pistachio green colour is clearly visible. The nuts are roasted in their shells before being salted and eaten. They are also used increasingly in patisserie.

It was not very long ago that the world production of these nuts was virtually entirely in the hands of growers in Asia Minor. Although Iran is still the chief producer, the United States has become the second largest, pushing Turkey into third place. When the American Ministry of Agriculture sent a few botanists to Russia and Persia in 1929 to collect seeds of local varieties of fruit and vegetables, no one suspected that America would become such a major pistachio producer. The expedition suffered many hardships, but finally returned with a large number of seeds, including those of *Pistacia vera*. The following year there were about 3,000 young seedlings in the United States.

It takes about seven to ten years for a pistachio tree cultivated from seed to bear fruit, and so the growers were only able to start the process of selecting the most productive seedlings in about 1945. In the end, there was only one promising specimen. An attempt was made to propagate this particular tree by grafting it onto young trunks. Initially the trunks were prone to fungal diseases, but eventually the growers succeeded in growing a good, fruit-bearing, female plant and a resistant trunk. Once a suitable male partner was found which flowered at the same time, all the obstacles had been overcome and the pistachio nut could be cultivated in the United States on a large scale. Tax incentives were provided to encourage cultivation, to help with the non-productive starting period of six to seven years, when the trees do not bear fruit. The pistachio nut became very popular. Oil companies in particular invested large sums in this new nut, and huge areas of California were transformed into pistachio nut plantations.

Between 1970 and 1979 the total area of all these plantations increased from 100 to 10,000 hectares, and in a period of three years the harvest went up from 70,000 to 8,000,000 kg.

It is expected that in the 1990s the total production in the United States will amount to 40–60,000,000kg. Probably this increase will mean that Iran will no longer be the chief producer. Certainly the botanists who collected the seeds in 1929 could never have foreseen these developments.

GROWING TIPS
Pistacia vera is not frost hardy, but it can be cultivated outdoors in summer. However, young pistachio nut plants are only very occasionally available from specialist nurseries. The seeds are also difficult to obtain. If you manage to procure some seeds, sow them in moist peat and place them in a warm spot, for example, on the windowsill. Do not repot the young seedlings into individual pots until the seed leaves have fully developed. Then when they are larger, you can transplant them into larger pots. They develop best in a rich, nutritious growing medium, consisting, for example, of equal parts of peat, soil, and old, well-rotted stable manure.

Place the plants outside on a sunny patio in large pots or wooden tubs during the summer months. In winter, keep them in a cool, frost-free place.

Plane Tree

Scientific name:	Platanus orientalis L.
Family name:	Platanaceae
Natural habitat:	the Lebanon, the Orient, Syria
English name:	plane tree
Biblical name:	plane tree
Hebrew name:	
Greek name:	

Jacob, however, took fresh-cut branches from poplar, almond and plane trees and made white stripes on them by peeling the bark and exposing the inner white wood of the branches.

GENESIS 30:37

The cedars in the garden of God could not rival it,
nor could the pine trees equal its boughs,
nor could the plane trees compare with its branches —
no tree in the garden of God could match its beauty.

EZEKIEL 31:8

The plane tree mentionned in the Bible is the *Platanus orientalis*, which is not often found in temperate countries. This oriental plane tree is sensitive to frost, unlike the common plane tree, *P. X acerifolia*, which is a hybrid of *P. occidentalis* and *P. orientalis*, and is planted along roads everywhere. Plane trees can grow to become enormous trees no less than 50m in height, and in some cases the diameter of the trunk can be over 15m. They are particularly striking in winter because of the different colours of the peeling bark. The new bark appears as lighter coloured patches because it has not yet been affected by dust, fumes and other pollution.

The flowers are round and puffy. They are followed by large, round fruits which hang down in bunches from the branches on long stalks. However, these only become visible when the leaves have fallen. When the fruit ripens, it splits open and the fluffy seeds are dispersed by the wind. *Platanus orientalis* is not unknown in the Orient, and is very common in the Lebanon, Syria and Israel. Although it grows mainly on plains, at the water's edge, or in wet areas, it is also found in mountainous, sub-Alpine areas.

In the Bible, the plane tree is usually mentioned together with willow trees and poplars, which prefer moist conditions. It is highly probable that there were far more plane trees in the Holy Land in Bible times than there are now. Certainly the oriental plane tree was much appreciated by the Persians, Greeks and Romans, as well as by the Israelites, for its thick foliage, which provided a cool and shady place, particularly in hot weather. The plane tree still serves this function in the parks and along the lanes of Mediterranean countries.

The plane tree is one of the so-called 'heartwood' trees. The dark brown heartwood is encased in a thick layer of reddish-white sapwood. Freshly felled timber has a distinctive, penetrating smell, rather like horse manure. When a cross-section is cut, the broad annual rings, separated by dark stripes, are clearly visible. The plane tree produces exceptionally beautiful timber which is used in the furniture industry because of its silky structure. It is also used to make veneers. However, the wood is fairly heavy, hard and tough, so it is difficult to work with. It dries out quickly and is not really very durable. Another disadvantage is that it tends to split easily.

GROWING TIPS

Because of the enormous size to which a plane tree can grow, it is not really a suitable tree for the back garden. It is only really suitable for growing along roads or to be planted on its own in large parks. It is particularly when the tree has sufficient room to develop fully that it can grow to majestic proportions of great beauty. The tree is propagated by layering or taking cuttings.

Almond

Scientific name: Prunus dulcis (Miller) D.A. Webb.
Family name: Rosaceae
Natural habitat: southern Europe, southern central
Europe and the Mediterranean area
English name: almond tree
Biblical name: almond

*When men are afraid of heights and of dangers in the streets;
when the almond tree blossoms and the grasshopper drags himself
along...*
ECCLESIASTES 12:5

The almond, *Prunus dulcis* (syn: *Amygdalus communis, P. amygdalus, P. communis*), belongs to the rose family (Rosaceae), and before being mentioned in the Bible was only found in the temperate parts of western India and Persia.

In ancient times, the valuable nuts produced by the tree were traded with costly spices. They were imported to many countries around the Mediterranean Sea, where almond trees have been cultivated since that time.

It may be assumed that they were not yet grown in Palestine when Jacob left to find grain in Egypt in about 1700 BC. Thus, the 'almonds' which he supposedly sent as a gift for the Pharaoh, according to Genesis 43:11 are an anachronism slipped in by a writer from a later age. In those days, almond trees had only been cultivated in Egypt for a short time. It was probably only when the Israelites stayed in Egypt that they really became familiar with the almond.

Jewish artists used the motif of the almond blossom and bud for the design of the golden candle-holder (Exodus 25: 31–40; 37: 17–24). The fact that they were familiar with almond wood at that time is also revealed in Numbers 17: 1–13, where Aaron's rod was carved from almond wood, blossoming and producing fruit in a very short space of time. It is well-known that the buds of bare almond branches which have been cut and placed in water will flower very quickly if they are placed in a warm spot; it is one of the woody plants that flowers most quickly. For that reason, the beautiful pink flowers symbolize the awakening of spring, and for the Jews they were the sign that winter had come to an end.

When the flowers have been pollinated, they form many ovaries which grow into almonds. The oval fruits are about 4cm long and surrounded by a thick, fleshy skin. The outside is covered in soft hair, rather like the stone of a peach. In about October, when the fruit is ripe, the fleshy casing divides lengthways into two parts, and the nuts are visible. They are ready to harvest in November, and when they have been dried, the soft kernel can be removed from the nut using a hammer. This is the almond we eat.

In addition, oil pressed from almonds is very popular because of its smooth taste. However, almonds which taste bitter contain a high proportion of poisonous prussic acid (cyanide).

GROWING TIPS

The almond is a valuable plant which should really be grown in every garden. It is cultivated both as a shrub and as a tree, though on a limited scale. If you want to buy an almond tree, it is important to order it from a garden centre or tree nursery in good time. The tree does not make any special demands as regards the composition of the soil, but it should be planted in a sunny spot.

In many cases it will grow so prolifically that it eventually takes up too much room, especially in smaller gardens. In this case, the tree must be pruned. The best time to do this is in the early spring before the buds open. The pruned branches can then be put in a vase to flower indoors. It is best to remove the branches which grow inwards in the centre of the crown, so that the crown has plenty of light and air. If you prune the tree too drastically, this encourages the development of so-called 'suckers'. These shoots can be more than 1m long, and will not flower, or hardly flower at all, the next year, but only a year later.

Almond trees cultivated in our gardens generally produce almonds which are too bitter for consumption. A few can be mixed with larger quantities of 'sweet' almonds to balance the taste; this is particularly recommended for making marzipan.

Almond trees are prone to so-called 'ear sickness'. This is a fungus which causes deformed leaves to develop in the shape of an ear. The disease does not damage the trees very much, and can only be treated with toxic preparations, so it is best not to try to treat it; there is a good chance that the fungus will have disappeared by the following year.

PRUNUS DULCIS

Pomegranate

Scientific name:	Punica granatum L.
Family name:	Punicaceae
Natural habitat:	southern Europe, Mediterranean area, Portugal
English name:	pomegranate
Biblical name:	pomegranate tree

Your plants are an orchard of pomegranates with choice fruits.
SONG OF SONGS 4:13

There is absolutely no doubt about the identity of the plant described in various passages in the Bible as a pomegranate. This is clear from the Hebrew name *rimmon* in the original version. It is also probable that the name of the city *Rimmonperez* or *Rimmon*, in the books of Numbers 30:19–20, Joshua 15:32, and Judges 20:45, refers to the large numbers of pomegranates which grew there.

Punica granatum is the only genus which represents the family of the Punicaceae. It is a fairly thorny large bush or small tree which loses its leaves and grows to a maximum height of about 10m. The long, oval, light green leaves grow in pairs on winged stems. The flowers develop singly, or sometimes in bunches of five, at the end of young twigs, and are 2–4cm in diameter. The calyx is fleshy and does not drop off, and the corolla is an orange-red colour. The spherical, juicy fruit have two cores, one above the other. They grow to a diameter of 10cm, and are surrounded by a hard red or yellow shell.

Initially indigenous to Asia, and probably originating from northeast India, the pomegranate has been cultivated since time immemorial. In the Holy Land, Egypt, and along the coast of the Mediterranean it is a common tree, cultivated on a large scale for its fruit. In Bible times the pomegranate was also highly prized. The juicy, slightly sour-tasting fruit was not only eaten fresh, but was also used in drinks. The skin of unripe fruit produces a red dye which was used for dyeing materials, and was also considered to have medicinal properties.

The Moors used the skin of the pomegranate for tanning leather, and introduced this method in Spain. In this way, Cordoba became famous for the fine quality of the leather articles produced there. Even in the very distant past the pomegranate was considered to be a holy plant. The large numbers of seeds in the fruit were associated with fertility.

GROWING TIPS
The pomegranate is not frost hardy, but it can be cultivated in a tub with little difficulty. Both the common pomegranate and the dwarf variety are available from well-stocked garden centres. Place the plant outside on a sunny patio in the summer months.

The first flowers will appear at the beginning of the summer, and provided they are fertilized by insects, they will develop into the prized pomegranates. In cooler climates it takes a long time for the fruit to ripen, and the process is only completed in the year after the fruit appears.

The plant must spend the winter in a cool, frost-free place from the beginning of autumn. As virtually all the leaves fall off, the light does not have to be very bright. If necessary, prune the plant in the autumn before moving it back indoors. Only repot it if the container has become too small for the roots. The best time to do this is a few weeks before moving the plant outdoors. The best growing medium to use in the pot is a mixture consisting of two parts of peat to one part of potting compost and one part of well-rotted manure.

In the course of the centuries some outstanding varieties have been cultivated, such as the double red flowering *Punica granatum* 'Plena', the double white *'Alba Plena'* (syn: *Punica granatum* 'Multiplex'); and 'Legrellei', which has full, orange-red flowers with yellowy-white edges. But of all these varieties, the most popular is *Punica granatum* 'Nana', a miniature variety which is even cultivated as a pot plant. This relatively slow-growing variety thrives best in a light, fairly cool room. The advantage of the dwarf variety is that it flowers more profusely, and also develops fruit more easily. True pomegranate varieties can be propagated from seed, but cultivated varieties must be propagated from cuttings. Use rooting preparations to encourage the cuttings to take root.

PUNICA GRANATUM

Oak

Scientific name: Quercus aegilops L.
Family name: Fagaceae
Natural habitat: Mediterranean area
English name: oak
Biblical name: oak

---

*But as the terebinth and oak leave stumps when they are cut
down, so the holy seed will be the stump in the land.*
ISAIAH 6:13

There were many varieties of oaks in the Holy Land,
even 3,000 years ago. All oaks belong to the genus
Quercus, of which there are about 450 different varieties
growing in North America, western South America and
the temperate and sub-tropical areas of Europe, Asia
and North Africa. They belong to the Fagaceae family,
of which the beech tree is also a member.

The oak is often mentioned in the Bible. There is
no doubt that these references are to evergreen varieties
such as *Quercus aegilops, Quercus coccifera, Quercus ilex,
Quercus lusitanica* and many others. These oaks were
highly prized for their robust, powerful growth and the
considerable age which they can attain. In many cases,
important people were buried in the shade of their
gigantic crowns. The trees played an important role in
the mythology and religion of many nations.

Most varieties which are found in the Holy Land
grow to an enormous size, well over 35m in height.

They produce hard and durable timber. The holm oak,
Quercus ilex, which is found throughout the
Mediterranean area, produces wood of rather dubious
quality.

The fruit of some varieties—the acorns—were
used as a source of food for animals and humans. The
cups containing the acorns, as well as the oak apples on
the leaves and young branches, were used for tanning
leather and for dyeing linen and wool. They were also
important in the manufacture of ink. In Bible times, the
lice which were found in huge numbers on the young
shoots were also collected and used to dye linen and
wool to produce a scarlet colour. Oaks were believed to
attract lightning more readily than other trees. This was
because they generally grow taller than other trees. It is
also the reason that farmers planted one or more oak
trees near their farmhouses, in order to be spared the
ravages of nature.

GROWING TIPS
Quercus ilex is the only Mediterranean variety which is
fairly hardy in winter in our climate. It is advisable to
protect young specimens from very severe frost during
the early stages, but as they grow bigger the resistance to
frost increases. The tree will live considerably longer in
a warm, fairly dry and above all, sunny spot.

Because of their leathery and rather coarse leaves
which evaporate little moisture, evergreen varieties of
oak from subtropical areas, such as the holm oak,
Quercus ilex, and the cork oak, *Quercus suber*, are suitable
for cultivation as pot plants. They should be placed in a
fairly warm spot where they will get plenty of light,
such as a conservatory.

Evergreen oak trees also thrive in tubs that are put
outdoors in summer. Repot the plant in the spring in
equal parts of peat and potting compost, adding a little
old, well-rotted manure. During the growing period,
feed the plant, by adding some artificial fertilizer to the
water once every three weeks.

Like virtually all oak trees, *Quercus ilex* is fairly easy
to grow from seed (acorns). Sometimes the tree is also
on sale as a young seedling.

QUERCUS SUBER

Rose

Scientific name: Rosa phoenicea Boiss
Family name: Rosaceae
Natural habitat: Turkey, Cyprus, the Lebanon
English name: rose
Biblical name: rose of Sharon

I am a rose of Sharon, a lily of the valleys.
SONG OF SONGS 2:1

It is a well known fact that the 'rose' in the text quoted above is often replaced by the word 'flower'. The many translations of the Song of Songs over the course of the centuries have often been tempted to use the names of well-known plants found growing wild or commonly cultivated in the country concerned. The rose of Sharon referred to here is not easy to identify with certainty, but is most probably the narcissus.

This does not, however, mean that there were no roses among the flora of the Holy Land at the time of the birth of Christ. On the contrary, several different varieties were known at the time. Modern translations of Ecclesiasticus 24:14 even refer to a rose bush. In any case, as the rose played an important role in earlier translations of the Bible, there is good reason to devote more attention to it here.

J.J. Scheuchzer's comprehensive work entitled *Spiritual Physics*, published in Amsterdam in 1785, is justifiably described as one of the most beautiful books of the baroque period because of its unusually fine copper engravings of Biblical scenes. It also contains pictures of Biblical plants. One of these depicts a 'rose of Sharon', according to the caption. The rose that is depicted is an eighteenth century, double-headed garden hybrid. The other plant shown with it also gives rise to some confusion when considered in the light of the indigenous flora of the Holy Land. The plant concerned is described as a 'yellow lily heath-flower' which is also occasionally found in a 'reddish-brown colour'. According to modern opinion, the reference is to hybrids of the day lily *(Hemerocallis)*, which was originally indigenous to Asia Minor. The plant that is depicted is very probably *Hemerocallis fulva*, a variety which blossoms with fairly large flowers and which was cultivated in abbey gardens in the Netherlands as early as 1567. Various other cultivated varieties of this flower were also known at that time. This is why Scheuchzer referred to the 'yellow and reddish-brown coloured' heath flower.

Earlier translators of the Bible had translated the rose of Sharon as the asphodil, a lily-like plant which belongs to the flora of the Holy Land. However, the varieties of this genus are much less beautiful than the *Hemerocallis* hybrids which were known in the 18th century. Hence the confusion which is so common in the many older versions with regard to translations of plant names in the Bible.

GROWING TIPS:
The rose is so popular as a garden plant and as a pot plant that we will not include a description of the method of cultivation here. For anyone who is interested and wants to know more, there is plenty of literature available in virtually every reasonably stocked bookshop. *Rosa phoenicea* is not hardy in winter. However, there are many other botanical varieties which resemble the rose mentioned here which are resistant to winter temperatures.

Madder

Scientific name: Rubia tinctorium L.
Family name: Rubiaceae
Natural habitat: Eastern Mediterranean area
English name: madder
Biblical name: scarlet

---

*Make the tabernacle with ten curtains of finely twisted linen
and blue, purple and scarlet yarn ...*
EXODUS 26:1

In Bible times, preparations for dyeing linen and wool
were made from insects, shellfish and plants. Dyeing
fabrics using animal and vegetable dyes was common
long before the ancient Egyptian, Persian and Indian
civilizations. However, it is assumed that at that time
the Israelites themselves were not familiar with the
preparation and processing of dyes. It is probable that
in this respect they were largely dependent on the
Phoenicians and Egyptians.

For example, the manufacture of the celebrated
purple dyes at that time was mainly carried out by the
people of Tyre, one of the most famous Phoenician
trading cities. The preparation of this purple dye,
which was made from the shells of certain molluscs,
was a carefully-guarded secret which was lost,
according to legend, when Alexander the Great
conquered Tyre in 322 BC. Some of the bluish-violet
hues were extracted by the Phoenicians from the scales
of certain species of fish which were found along their
coasts.

However, most dyes were made from plants. For
example, henna *(Lawsonia inermis)* produced a yellow,
orange or red colour; the indigo bush *(Indigofera tinctoria)*
produced blue; woad *(Isatis tinctoria)* produced yellow
and blue and the safflower *(Carthamus tinctorius)*
produced yellow and orange-red. Lichens such as *Rocella
tinctoria* (blue) were also used to manufacture dyes. The
scientific name of all these species, *tinctorius*, shows that
these are plants used for making dyes: the Latin word
'tinctor' means painter.

The scarlet dye referred to in the Bible text quoted
above was already used at the time of the Patriarchs in
about 1750 BC. At that time, various shades of red,
orange and brown were obtained from the roots of
madder *(Rubia tinctorium)*. This plant, which belongs to
the *Rubiaceae* family, has been cultivated in the
Netherlands, particularly in Zeeland, on a large scale
since the sixteenth century. It is a perennial plant which
is hardy in winter, and produces roots which can be
harvested after two or three years. They were used to
make dye when they had been fermented. When the
roots had been lifted, they were first dried in the wind,
and then in ovens at a temperature of 50–60° C. Then
they were scrubbed and broken. When it became
possible to prepare the dye chemically in 1868 the
cultivation of this plant declined noticeably and
eventually disappeared altogether.

GROWING TIPS:
Madder is easy to cultivate from seed which is available
from specialized seed merchants. However, it is easier
to buy young plants, which are more commonly
available now that dyeing has become more popular.

Madder makes little or no demands as regards the
composition of the soil as long as it is well drained, as
the roots—for which the plant is primarily grown—
would otherwise rot away.

Sorrel

Scientific name: Rumex acetosa L.
Family name: Polygonaceae
Natural habitat: Europe, Asia
English name: common sorrel
Biblical name: bitter herbs

They are to celebrate it on the fourteenth day of the second month at twilight. They are to eat the lamb, together with unleavened bread and bitter herbs.

NUMBERS 9:11

The Jews used many herbs for the Passover meal; they had originally collected these during their trip through the desert. However, it is by no means certain that all the plants which are used now under the collective name 'bitter herbs' were also collected for this purpose in Bible times.

Certainly the bitter herbs included common sorrel (*Rumex acetosa*) and sheep's sorrel (*Rumex acetosella*). These both have a very large natural habitat that extends quite far north into Europe.

The genus *Rumex*, the old Latin name for sorrel, which was adopted by Linnaeus, comprises 200 varieties which are members of the Polygonaceae family. The name of the species *acetosa*, and the diminutive form of this, *acetosella*, are derived from the Latin word *acetum*, 'vinegar', which clearly refers to the sour taste of the leaves.

RUMEX ACETOCELLA

At first glance, *Rumex acetosella* or sheep's sorrel is simply a smaller variety of *Rumex acetosa*. Moreover, *Rumex acetosella* is found particularly in arid, sandy soil, and in poor, dry peatland, where it can spread prolifically by means of its long roots which grow on the surface and form shoots everywhere above the ground, in and out of season. When they grow in large clumps, the plants attract attention from a great distance because of the striking green and dark red colours which appear in the landscape, the latter especially during the autumn. As a rule, the plants only grow to a height of 15–20cm, but they are among the most dreaded and most difficult root weeds to eradicate, along with, for example, horsetail *(Equisetum arvense)*, couch grass *(Agropyron repens)*, and ground elder *(Aegopodium podagraria)*.

Common sorrel is quite different. This plant is larger in every respect (50–125cm) and does not form long suckers, but grows in fairly compact clumps. During the spring it is a very common plant adorning roadside verges, together with buttercups, cow parsley, and other plants, and striking because of its large numbers of red, dark red and sometimes greenish-white plumes. Both varieties are found throughout the temperate and cold regions of the northern and southern hemispheres. They are dioecious: the male and female flowers grow on different plants. Fertilization is carried out by means of the wind. The broad-winged fruit dispersed by the wind or by animals is characteristic of *Rumex acetosa*. In *Rumex acetosella*, the fruit casing does not grow any longer than the ripe fruit.

One delicious dish prepared with this plant is sorrel soup. Sorrel is a vegetable which deserves far more appreciation and popularity than it has at the moment.

The last leaves to develop are not cut; this gives the plant a chance to gather strength for the next season, in the same way as rhubarb, which actually belongs to the same family. In order to harvest a good crop of leaves, it is important to make sure that the tender leaves are not devoured by the ever-greedy slugs.

GROWING TIPS

Sorrel is very easy to grow, particularly as it does not make any demands on the soil. About ten seedlings will be more than enough to provide as much leaf as you could possibly need.

Sow the seeds in the early spring. As a rule, the young plants will rapidly develop, planted about 30 cm apart, and the first leaves can be harvested after about three months. This should be done very thoroughly. In the same way as spinach is harvested, this plant should also be cut in its entirety about 1cm above the ground. When the plants are a year old, this can be repeated once more, up to the end of summer. If you do it more than once, the part of the plant that is under the ground will fail to spread and the roots will die off. When the plants are several years old, they can be harvested several times up to the end of summer. New leaves will develop every time that the plant is cut, and these can then be harvested when they are fully grown.

Butcher's Broom

Scientific name: Ruscus aculeatus L.
Family name: Ruscaceae (Liliaceae)
Natural habitat: western, southern and central
                     southern Europe
English name: butcher's broom
Biblical name: briers

And you, son of man, do not be afraid of them or their words.
Do not be afraid, though briers and thorns are all around you
and you live among scorpions . . .

EZEKIEL 2:6

Nettles, thorns, thistles and briers are mentioned in many Bible texts, and there are many plants to which these could refer. Butcher's broom (*Ruscus aculeatus*) is undoubtedly an important member of this group.

It is difficult to ascertain the derivation of the name *Ruscus*. Apparently it was an old Latin plant name which has existed for a long time. The name of the species *aculeatus* is derived from the Latin word *aculeus*, which

means 'thorn' or 'thorny'. The genus, which comprises three different species, was included in the lily family (Liliaceae) for a long time. However, with modern nomenclature it became necessary to include the genus in a separate family, Ruscaceae.

In this family, *Ruscus* is the best known genus. *Ruscus aculeatus* is a popular Christmas plant, when the female branches are covered in red berries the size of a large pea. They contrast attractively with the dark green of the prickly leaves which are not actually leaves in a botanical sense, but so-called 'phylloclades' or scale-shaped leaves. Each of these phylloclades can produce one or several small greenish flowers, which develop into attractive red berries when they have been pollinated by a male plant growing in the vicinity.

Ruscus branches are sold even without these single-seed berries. When they are dry, they are dipped in paint, to restore their original dark green colour. Then they are often dipped in a tray of coloured styrofoam grains. When they have been treated like this, many of the coloured balls stick to the painted scale-shaped leaves and this is how the branches are sold. These kitsch decorations can be kept for years.

Another member of this genus, *Ruscus hypoglossum*, is used slightly differently. Twigs of this plant have been imported in large quantities for several years to be used as greenery in combination with the leafless flowering branches of *Cymbidium* orchids.

RUSCUS ACULEATUS

Cymbidium keeps for a long time, but the branches of *Ruscus hypoglossum* last even longer, and will even keep for several months, in water.

In contrast with *Ruscus aculeatus*, all the parts of *Ruscus hypoglossum* are softer. The plant does not have such prickly leaves and is not so tough. Butcher's broom itself is fairly impenetrable for animals and humans, and travelling through an area where these plants grow is no mean feat. It usually ends in torn clothes and deep scratches. Butcher's broom grows prolifically in the countries surrounding the Mediterranean. The young stems are sometimes eaten in the same way as asparagus is here. In more temperate climates the various species of butcher's broom are rarely cultivated.

GROWING TIPS

The plants of the two *Ruscus* varieties mentioned here were first introduced to the Netherlands by the herbalist Clusius in 1594. Although they are not entirely frost hardy, they generally thrive in the garden if they are properly covered in winter. The plant is not fussy with regard to the composition of the soil, although it prefers a fairly heavy clay soil to a light, sandy soil.

The plants eventually reach a height of about 50–75cm, and will grow either in the shade or in the full sun. They can be propagated either from seed, or by dividing the plant. If you grow it from seed, it may in some cases take more than a year for the large, hard seeds to germinate. After this, the development is slow before the plant will flower. It can take about five years before the first flowers appear.

Rue

Scientific name: Ruta graveolens L.
Family name: Rutaceae
Natural habitat: southern and central southern Europe,
                     the Balkan Peninsula and the Crimea
English name: rue
Biblical name: rue

---

*Woe to you, Pharisees, because you give God a tenth of your
mint, rue and other kinds of garden herbs, but you neglect justice
and the love of God.*

LUKE 11:42

It is fairly certain that the rue referred to in Luke belongs to the genus *Ruta*. However, it is not entirely clear which particular species is meant. There are no fewer than sixty different *Rutas,* most of which grow wild in Mediterranean countries, while a small number are found in the temperate regions of Asia. *Ruta chalepensis* and *Ruta graveolens* are the best known varieties in the Holy Land.

Ruta chalepensis is the wild plant indigenous to the Bible lands. *Ruta graveolens* did not grow wild as much there, but was specially cultivated. Both plants are small shrubs which can grow to a height of 40–70cm. They emit a striking, penetrating odour which is quite unmistakable to anyone who comes near. The leaves, stems and other parts of the plant contain a great deal of volatile oil which is released in quantity during hot weather, or if the plant is touched.

Rue was highly prized as a medicinal herb in

RUTA
GRAVEOLENS

ancient times. Centuries ago, it was considered as a preventive remedy for all sorts of contagious diseases. It was even imagined that you could drive out an incipient disease simply by inhaling the odour. *Ruta* was also known as a contraceptive remedy. The story goes that when girls had been led astray, they could safeguard themselves from the consequences of their actions by eating the leaves of a rue plant.

The healing power attributed to the plant was based primarily on its strong odour, and not, or to a lesser extent, on demonstrable medicinal properties. Many people are in fact allergic to contact with rue. It causes skin rashes which heal very slowly.

Rue is still known as a culinary herb. The strongly aromatic, slightly bitter leaves can be used to season sauces for meat and fish dishes, and in the preparation of soup. When it is dried, rue loses its odour, but not its taste.

GROWING TIPS
Ruta chalepensis cannot really tolerate winter frost.

However, *Ruta graveolens* thrives in cooler climates and is a valuable plant in the garden and quite undemanding to grow. It will flourish in any soil and is easy to grow from seed.

Sow the seed indoors in the early spring, and then repot and plant outdoors in early summer, or sow the seeds directly into the ground when the soil has warmed up. The plants will usually flower the same year with large numbers of yellowish-green flowers arranged in a sort of umbel.

As the plants become more established, they grow more beautiful, especially if the dead flowering stalks are removed in the early spring. This produces a bushy and compact plant. The flowering stems can be cut and keep in water for a long time, and when they have finished flowering, these flowering stalks, which have large seedpods, can be dried and are extremely decorative when combined with other dried flowers.

Finally, it is said that one or two rue plants in the garden will keep cats away. Having tried this, I can assure you that it is nonsense.

Sarcopoterium

Scientific name: Sarcopoterium spinosum (L.) Stach.
Family name: Rosaceae
Natural habitat: the Mediterranean area
English name: burnet
Biblical name: thornbush

Therefore I will block her path with thornbushes; I will wall her in so that she cannot find her way.

HOSEA 2:6

Sarcopoterium spinosum (syn. *Poterium spinosum*) is a well-known plant in the so-called *maquis*, the dry regions in the Mediterranean countries where the soil consists of chalk. It is a dense, thorny shrub which reaches a maximum height of about 60cm. The composite leaves consist of 9–15 pairs of dentate leaf segments which quickly drop off.

Every young shoot splits into two thorny branches which die away every year after they have first produced flowers and fruit. Depending on the weather conditions, the shrub blossoms between March and May. The round or oval flower heads are about 3cm long and are composed of diclinous flowers. The female flowers, which are at the top, consist mainly of feathery, purple pistils; the greenish male flowers are just below them.

The bright red, fleshy, composite achenes are much more striking than the flowers. Each segment contains two to three seeds.

Sarcopoterium spinosum is a plant which is highly resistant to the extreme conditions which prevail in its natural habitat. Often it is the only vegetation to survive after a long period of drought or after a fire. Although the dry shrubs burn very well, new shoots quickly form from the base. The branches are easy to handle because of their fine and flexible structure. They used to be collected for fuel on a large scale, particularly for use in lime kilns and ovens. The branches were also used as coarse filters in water basins.

Dioscorides described the medicinal properties of the leaves and seeds. An infusion of these was used to prevent dysentery, sores, haemorrhages, and bloodshot eyes. As the plant grew prolifically in the vicinity of Jerusalem in ancient times, it has been supposed that Christ's crown of thorns was made from its branches.

GROWING TIPS

Sarcopoterium spinosum is not really hardy to winter frosts. It will only survive for a while in an extremely dry, warm spot, for example, in a rockery, but then only if the winters are mild. However, this perennial shrub can easily be grown from seed, and develops best in good, well-drained growing medium consisting, for example, of equal parts of soil and sand.

During the summer months the pots should be placed outside in the garden in a sunny, warm spot. In winter, bring the plants into a cool, light room. During the winter months, keep the earth in the pot fairly dry.

SARCOPOTERIUM SPINOSUM

Golden Thistle

Scientific name:	Scolymus maculatus L.
Family name:	Compositae
Natural habitat:	Southern Europe
English name:	golden thistle
Biblical name:	thorn

Thorns will overrun her citadels, nettles and brambles her strongholds...
ISAIAH 34:13

Thorns, nettles and thistles include some varieties which are native over a wide area of Europe. These include Our Lady's thistle *(Silybum marianum)*, the star thistle *(Centaurea calcitrapa)*, and the large and small stinging nettle (respectively *Urtica dioica* and *U. urens)*. The Spanish oyster plant or golden thistle *(Scolymus maculatus)* belongs to the *Compositae* family. It is occasionally found growing in more northerly parts of Europe but is an adventive plant, which means that its natural habitat is in another country. The name of the genus, *Scolymus,* is derived from an old Greek plant name which related to a thistle-like plant with an edible flower receptacle or base, probably the artichoke. The scientific name of the genus of the artichoke is *Cynara,* and it was given the name *Scolymus* to indicate the species. It is well known that the base of the artichoke is edible, but this is not the case with the Spanish oyster plant, because the flower base is much smaller and contains hardly anything worth eating. However, in this case it is the roots which can be eaten, particularly when they are not too old.

Scolymus maculatus, which is found everywhere in dry soil in Mediterranean countries, can grow into a dense plant with sharp thorns, about 50–60cm tall in dry, sunny weather conditions. The strong, tough leaves have silvery-white, horny edges with occasional white spots *(maculatus* means 'spotted').

When the plant is flowering, it is very striking because of the large numbers of golden yellow flowers, to which it owes its popular name, Golden Thistle. It grows as a biennial plant in the wild, though gardeners treat it as an annual. In a damp climate it can grow more than 1m tall. The drier and sunnier the spot, and the poorer the soil, the smaller the plant will be, and the more profusely it will flower.

SCOLYMUS MACULATUS

GROWING TIPS

Sow the plant in late spring in reasonably nutritious soil which has been dug over in advance so that it is well drained and the taproots can grow straight. It will be a delightful ornamental feature, because of its abundant golden flowers.

When you lift the roots in the autumn, it is essential to wear gloves, because of the extremely sharp thorns which cover the whole plant. The roots must be lifted before the first frost to prevent them from being frozen. Then store them in a frost-free place in a heap in moist sand until the end of winter.

Our Lady's Thistle

Scientific name: Silybum marianum (L.) Gaertner
Family name: Compositae
Natural habitat: Mediterranean area and southwest Europe
English name: Our Lady's thistle
Biblical name: brambles

Thorns will overrun her citadels, nettles and brambles her strongholds.
ISAIAH 34:13

It is not always possible to determine exactly which plants are referred to in passages in the Bible. In this case, there is a reference to thorns and brambles, and it is difficult to ascertain exactly which species are meant. However, it is possible to find out fairly accurately which species originally grew in the Holy Land, and which were only introduced later on. Thistles which were common in Bible times are still found growing profusely in Israel nowadays. One of the most spectacular species is Our Lady's thistle, *Silybum marianum*.

The name of the genus *Silybum* is derived from the ancient Greek word *silubon* or *silubos*, which was the name of a type of thistle. The name of the species *marianus* refers to Mary, the mother of Jesus. According to legend, the white spots on the leaves were caused by the milk which dripped onto the plant from her breasts when she was feeding Jesus. Because of this, the plant was considered to be sacred and to have healing properties.

Our Lady's thistle or milk thistle was particularly valued as a medicinal herb in the past. An infusion of the seeds was used for protection against disorders of the lungs, liver and gall bladder, as well as haemorrhages of the womb and dropsy.

It belongs to the Compositae family and was originally indigenous to an area stretching from the Mediterranean as far as the Caucasus and Iran. It was also introduced in other countries and has become widespread in the pampas of South America, and is sometimes found growing wild in northern Europe along roadsides, on compost heaps, and in kitchen gardens as well as ornamental gardens. The plant has been cultivated since 1542.

It is an annual, and sometimes a biennial, and can grow to a height of 75–200cm, depending on the composition of the soil. The rather leathery leaves grow in tight rosettes. They have white spots along the veins and yellow thorns along the edges. The young leaves are edible when the sharp thorns are removed and they are mixed with other vegetables. When the plant is ready to flower, one or more flowering stalks develop from the heart with the stalk enclosed in leaves. The large flowers grow at the end of these, about 4–5cm in diameter. The flowers are purplish-red or sometimes white, and are protected by leathery enveloping leaves, each with a sharp thorn. These sharp thorns along the edges of the leaves, stalks and enveloping leaves of the flowers keep animals and humans at a distance.

GROWING TIPS

The seed of Our Lady's thistle, which will grow in any soil, can be sown at two different times of the year: spring or late summer. If the winters are not too severe, it is better to sow the seed later on, because late seedlings have a chance to grow into large plants before the winter and will grow on vigorously the following year. By contrast, the plants sown in the spring will remain a great deal smaller. In either case, the plants will flower from late summer to mid autumn.

It is best to leave a good space between each seed, as the plants grow so tall. It is difficult to replant seedlings because they have a large tap root and a small number of side roots. In some cases you will have to support these large plants, to prevent them from being blown over.

You can only extract the seeds when the flowers turn into fluff. Cut off the flower heads and leave them to ripen in a dry place out of the sun. The fairly large, smooth seeds can then be cleaned easily.

SILYBUM MARIANUM

Styrax Tree

Scientific name: Styrax officinalis L.
Family name: Styracaceae
Natural habitat: eastern Mediterranean area to
western central Italy
English name: styrax tree
Biblical name: gum resin

---

*Then the Lord said to Moses, 'Take fragrant spices—gum resin,
onycha and galbanum—and pure frankincense, all in equal
amounts.'*

EXODUS 30:34

The sweet-smelling gum resin which was traded on a large scale in Bible times was also known as amber or myrrh. Amber was extracted from the amber tree, and myrrh from *Commiphora myrrha*. However, the gum resin referred to in the text quoted above may well have come from the styrax tree *(Styrax officinalis)*, a woody plant which belongs to the Styracaceae family.

This shrub is the only member of the *Styrax* genus which has its natural habitat in Mediterranean countries. Approximately 130 other species grow wild, particularly in Asia, as far as the Indo-Malaysian archipelago. Some species have even penetrated as far as Central America and the United States. In addition to the styrax tree, several other species also produce sweet-smelling resin, for example, *Styrax benzoin,* which is indigenous to Asia, produces the once well-known gum benzoin when the bark is cut.

Styrax gum and gum benzoin are closely related, and they are also sold under other names. When the yellowish liquid has been collected, it sets as a glassy brownish-grey resin which emits a pleasant odour because of the benzoic and cinnamic acids it contains. It is only possible to collect the sap from the styrax about seven years after the tree is planted. It is collected by cutting V-shaped incisions into the bark, and this can be repeated every three months. After being 'bled' intensely in this way, the shrub or tree will eventually die after ten or twelve years.

The gum from the styrax tree was imported from Asia to the Middle East and traded there, together with other spices, long before the birth of Christ. Combined with other aromatic substances, it formed an important constituent of many forms of frankincense. The gum was also used in the preparation of medicines, particularly in cough mixtures and ointments for rheumatism. In addition, it was widely used in the perfume industry.

STYRAX OFFICINALIS

GROWING TIPS

Styrax officinalis is a rare shrub. The bush, which comes from the Mediterranean, will do reasonably well in our climate if you plant it in a warm, sunny spot, provided that winter temperatures do not fall below -5 C. Nearly all Styrax varieties feel most at home in a warm, sunny spot. They have a preference for soil that is free of chalk and retains moisture. When planting the shrub, it should be remembered that specimens which are purchased fairly small eventually grow into large bushes, which might take up too much space, especially in smaller gardens.

Styrax japonica is a closely related, better known variety which is hardy in winter and will do better in gardens. It is indigenous to China, Japan and Korea, and can grow into a large bush or small tree of 4–7m.

The large, snowy-white pendent flowers, which appear in large numbers in early summer, come into their own best if the shrub is planted in such a way that you can clearly see under the branches. They look even better on specimens grafted onto a trunk. When the flowers have been pollinated, pea-sized fruit appear which dangle elegantly in the wind on long stalks. The seeds are poisonous. In areas where the tree grows wild, fishermen used to grind them up and cast the powder on the water so that the fish were drugged and easy to catch.

In addition to the varieties mentioned here, there are others which are cultivated as garden shrubs.

Dandelion

Scientific name: Taraxacum officinale Weber
Family name: Compositae
Natural habitat: worldwide
English name: dandelion
Biblical name: bitter herbs

That same night they are to eat the meat roasted over the fire,
along with bitter herbs, and bread made without yeast.
EXODUS 12:8

There are quite a few plants described as 'bitter herbs' in the Bible. We know from experience that when they are eaten raw, the leaves of dandelions, chicory and endive have a rather bitter taste. Lettuce, which also belongs to this group of vegetables, is nowadays rather less so, the bitter taste being a feature of the wild varieties. In the course of the centuries many different varieties have been developed, and as a consequence the bitter taste has gradually disappeared through selection. However, if the cultivated varieties start to form a stalk, the leaves that grow on it are still bitter.

The dandelion *(Taraxacum officinale),* the leaves of which can be eaten as a vegetable, is actually appreciated for its bitter taste by people who like salads. The cultivated dandelion has been bred from the ordinary wild dandelion, a very common indigenous perennial plant with fairly thick, long, heavy taproots. Jewish communities eat the young leaves of this plant, sometimes mixed with other bitter herbs, at the Passover meal. In fact, it is by no means certain that there were dandelions in the Holy Land in Bible times. However, we can assume that at that time there were many composite flowers which were picked and eaten under the name 'bitter herbs'.

GROWING TIPS

It is possible to sow cultivated dandelions in any soil directly into the garden at the end of spring. Alternatively, you can sow them in a special seedbed and set out the young plants in lines in loosely packed soil in early summer. The roots obtained in this way will guarantee a good crop of leaves.

In order to make sure that the rather tough leaves are more tender, they can be blanched several weeks before the harvest. You can do this by shielding the plant from light, perhaps covering them with a wooden box. Before blanching the plant it is important to make sure that it is dry. If the leaves are wet, they will easily rot and the harvest will fail.

To ensure that you have plenty of fresh dandelion leaves during the winter months as well, dig them up before the first frosts, with their roots, which have developed into long, straight taproots as a result of the soil being loosely packed when the plants were transplanted. You can clamp them in a frost-free, dark place, and force them in the same way as chicory.

After the harvest the roots can be kept in a frost-free place until the next season. During the harvest it may happen that part of the root is cut away with the leaves. These damaged roots do not have to be thrown away, as they will soon develop again.

TARAXACUM OFFICINALE

Tulip

Scientific name: Tulipa montana Lindley
Family name: Liliaceae
Natural habitat: Turkmenskaya and Iran
English name: tulip
Biblical name: rose of Sharon

I am a rose of Sharon, a lily of the valleys.
SONG OF SONGS 2:1

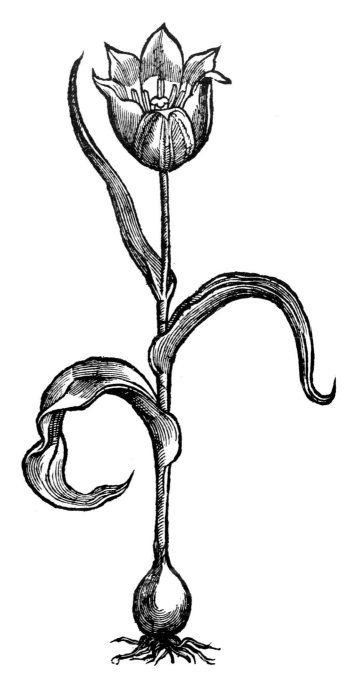

Some of the candidates for the name 'rose of Sharon' are dealt with in the entry for roses. Another plant which could make a less controversial claim is the tulip. Not just any tulip, but one which is nowadays counted among the group of botanical tulips. This is a collective name for real tulip varieties which still grow wild in some southern European countries and in Asia Minor. In most cases these are varieties with small flowers, which attract attention because of the beautiful shape of the flower, as well as the leaves, which can be elegantly curved.

In Iran, where several varieties of tulip can be found growing wild, special tulip festivals were organized in honour of the Sultan. The name *Tulipa* is derived from the Turkish word *tulbend* or the Persian word *dulband*. As the name indicates, the flower rather resembles a turban.

Tulipa montana and *Tulipa sharonensis* are the two varieties traditionally found in the Holy Land. As in other places, wild tulips are sold by children to tourists on roadsides during the flowering season, in mid-March. Usually they are pulled out of the ground with their leaves, which means that the bulbs remaining in the soil, sometime at a depth of 40–50cm, are badly affected. It is all the more remarkable that they reappear the following year, even if they do not always flower.

The above-mentioned varieties of tulip are very rarely grown in gardens. On the other hand, there are many other botanical varieties available. For anyone who likes these plants, it is certainly worth trying to grow them. They are usually available in autumn at a reasonable price from well-stocked garden centres. One of the favorite varieties is *Tulipa clusiana*, which produces extremely attractive red and white flowers on tall, slender stems. To make a real impact, at least twenty-five should be planted close together (approximately 2–3cm apart). This is easy to do because the bulbs are only the size of a large pea.

GROWING TIPS

In the wild, most tulips grow in stony clay soil which dries out considerably after the growing period. In places with more rainfall, it is best to dig up tulips when they have died away, and to store them in a dry place until they are ready to be planted out in autumn. However, botanical tulips can remain in a permanent position for a few years, provided they are planted in well-drained soil. Varieties with small flowers are particularly suitable for planting on rockeries. However, after some years, the bulbs divide up into several segments and no more flowers are produced.

Stinging-nettle

Scientific name: Urtica pilulifera L.
Family name: Urticaceae
Natural habitat: southern Europe
English name: stinging-nettle
Biblical name: nettle

And you, son of man, do not be afraid of them or their words.
Do not be afraid, though briers and thorns are all around you
and you live among scorpions.

EZEKIEL 2:6

There are many passages in the Bible which mention nettles, thorns and thistles. In most cases it is difficult to ascertain exactly which plant is being referred to.

A characteristic feature of stinging-nettles is that although they have no thorns or prickles, if you touch them, you quickly withdraw and usually feel some pain. This is caused by the large numbers of stinging hairs covering the surface of the leaf. These hairs are barely visible with the naked eye, but under a microscope they look like long, hollow, needle-shaped cells, with a curved, slightly thickened point. The base of every hair is pear-shaped and surrounded by leaf cells, together forming a cup. At the slightest touch, the tip of the hair breaks off diagonally at a place that is clearly visible under the microscope. The broken wall of the cell of the hair, which is very sharp, penetrates the skin so that the poisonous liquid in the middle of the stinging hair penetrates the subcutaneous tissue. The combination of the sharp tip of the hair and the poisonous content of the cell causes an itchy, burning feeling.

The poison, which is chemically very similar to snake venom, is very powerful.

The genus *Urtica*—an old Latin plant name derived from *urere*, 'to burn'—which belongs to the stinging-nettle family (Urticaceae), comprises about fifty different species, most of which can be found in the northern hemisphere. A distinction can be made between the annual varieties and perennials. *Urtica dioica*, the large stinging-nettle which belongs to the latter group, is found wherever there are people. The nettles particularly grow in places which are rich in nitrogen, where they can sometimes reach a height of 3m. They are usually considered a nuisance and as obstinate weeds which are difficult to eradicate because of their long, creeping rootstocks, some of which always remains in the ground. Nevertheless, the plant also has useful properties. While the shoots are young, they can be eaten in the same way as spinach. Before cotton was introduced into Europe, the fibres of the stems were used for a long time for the manufacture of muslin. In addition, fresh stinging-nettle stems were used as a remedy against rheumatism.

Urtica dioica is usually a dioecious plant, with male and female flowers on different stems, and sometimes provides an interesting spectacle in mid- to late summer. On hot summer days the male flower explodes as it opens. The curved pistils then stretch out so suddenly that there is a small cloud of pollen, which is blown by the wind to a flowering female plant.

The small nettle, *Urtica urens*, is an annual monoecious plant which grows to a height of about 60cm and is less common than the large stinging-nettle.

Urtica pilulifera is a monoecious annual plant, sometimes found as an adventive specimen in northern Europe. It grows to a height of about 100cm. In Mediterranean countries this variety is very commonly found in fallow fields near ruins and compost heaps. This species can be distinguished from the others by the many round fruits, about 1cm in diameter, which form at the end of the stems.

GROWING TIPS

The attractive, flat, shiny black seeds of *Urtica pilulifera* are similar to flax seeds, and contain oil, so they retain the capacity to germinate longer than other seeds. Sow them into the open soil at the end of spring. The quality of the soil is not particularly important. The seeds will germinate quickly, and this is followed by enormous growth. At the end of the growing season, the leaves turn yellow and drop off, and the round fruit really comes into its own, especially when the autumn sun catches it at a particular angle.

URTICA PILULIFERA

Broad Bean

Scientific name: Vicia faba L.
Family name: Leguminosae
Natural habitat: Caspian Sea area, northern Africa
English name: broad bean
Biblical name: bean

Take wheat and barley, beans and lentils, millet and spelt; put them in a container and make them into bread for yourself.
EZEKIEL 4:9

Vicia faba (syn: *Faba vulgaris*) is better known by its English name, broad bean. It does not play a very important role in the Bible. Perhaps this is because of the fact that at the time that this book of books was written, beans were not very popular amongst the more prosperous classes.

It was imagined that eating beans led to nightmares and encouraged improper behaviour. Merely dreaming about beans could cause problems, and even spirits were said to flee anxiously when they caught the scent of beans. The ancient Roman gods of the growth of plants, particularly the goddess of grain, Ceres, refused to include beans amongst their gifts to humanity. Even Hippocrates (460–377 BC), who is sometimes viewed as the father of medicine, fully believed that visual perception was adversely affected by eating broad beans. The Roman priests believed they were unclean, heathen food. Despite all this, broad beans nowadays constitute an important source of food which is highly valued by many people.

Vicia faba is an annual plant which belongs to the papilionaceous family (Leguminosae), and was probably originally indigenous to Iran. At a very early stage it was widely cultivated for food in western Asia and North Africa, so that it is not possible to be quite sure of its exact country of origin. Broad beans were also grown in ancient Egypt, as indicated by the fact that they were found with mummies. In the Holy Land, broad beans were an important item of diet, at least for the poorer people. As in Bible times, today they are still ground to make flour for baking bread.

There are many different cultivated varieties of *Vicia faba*, including a variety with very small beans. The seeds of this variety are mixed with grains and corn and used to feed pigeons and other poultry.

GROWING TIPS

It is easy to grow broad beans. You can sow the seeds outdoors in the open ground in spring, as one of the first vegetables. If you wish to have an early harvest, you can also sow the beans indoors in late winter in a seedbox, and then plant out the seedlings in spring when they are about 5cm tall. They will still have to be protected against night frost.

As the young tips of the plants are often attacked by blackfly, it is a good idea to remove the tops above the first six or seven flowers. In this way it is not necessary to use chemical preparations which can be poisonous.

The first pods are ready to harvest when they are still quite small. They contain small beans, which have the best flavour. When the beans are fully grown, they do not taste as good, because they contain much more starch.

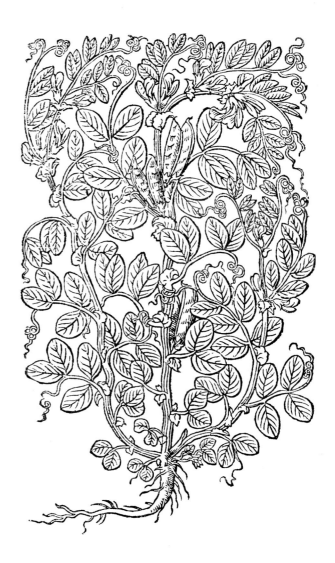

Vine

Scientific name: Vitis vinifera L.
Family name: Vitaceae
Natural habitat: the Caucasus, California
English name: vine
Biblical name: vine

Noah, a man of the soil, proceeded to plant a vineyard.
GENESIS 9:20–21

There are many references in the Bible to the ordinary grape *(Vitis vinifera)* from the story of Noah up to the time of Jesus. Like the olive, the grape was very important in those days. It was a symbol of the Jewish people. Jesus said: 'I am the true vine and my Father is the gardener. He cuts off every branch in me that bears no fruit, while every branch that does bear fruit he trims clean so that it will be even more fruitful' (John 15:1–2).

The vine is a woody plant with branches which can grow to a length of over 20m. The main trunk can be fairly thick; the wood is tough and flexible and covered with a fibrous, peeling, cork-like bark. Depending on the variety, the leaves are heart-shaped, with three or five lobes, sometimes with a hairy surface underneath, and the edges of the leaves are markedly dentate. The fruit differs greatly, depending on the variety, both in shape and in colour, which can vary from dark to light or yellowish green to a dark or light red, purple or blue. Over the course of the centuries countless varieties have been cultivated, not only selected for the size of the fruit, the taste or the yield, but also depending on the composition of the soil and climatic conditions.

Grapes were cultivated by the ancient Egyptians, as we see from the art dating from that period. The vine was probably the first Bible plant to be cultivated on a large scale. Since ancient times, virtually every civilization has grown grapes in every climate, so that it is very difficult to ascertain where the vine actually originated. It is assumed that it was growing in France by about 540 BC, and was then grown by the Romans in other parts of southern Europe. The latitude within which vines can be successfully be grown outdoors is approximately between the 36th and 48th parallels, but this does not mean that the plant is not found elsewhere. For example, in Norway, grapes ripen on the banks of the Sognefjord as far north as 61° N.

Vines rarely grow higher than 530m above sea level. The soil in which they grow varies from volcanic ash to chalk and sandstone soil. In general, heavier soils produce wines of a lesser quality, while the best quality grapes are harvested from lighter, and even poor soils. Ultimately, top quality wines are produced by a harmonious relationship between grape variety, soil composition, climate, the state of the vineyard and the skill of the wine-grower. However, of all the wines made throughout the world, only a very small proportion are truly great; the vast majority are suitable only for local consumption.

In Bible times, vines were usually grown in the vineyards situated on slopes. They were generally surrounded by high or low stone walls to keep out wild animals and thieves. There were also often stone towers between the walls to guard over the vineyard. At first the vines were grown so that they crept over rocks and walls, and were only later trained or cultivated as bushes. They were also often grown over porches, so that you could sit under your vine in the shade at the hottest time of day.

In the northern hemisphere, vines flower in May or at the beginning of June; in the southern hemisphere, in about November or December. Grapes need about four months to develop and ripen, so they are harvested in September/October in the north or in March/April in the south.

In Bible times the grape harvest started in September, and as in so many cultures, it was accompanied by festivities. During the harvest the towns were virtually empty because everyone went to the vineyards to help, staying in tents temporarily pitched in the vicinity of the vineyards. The best grapes were eaten fresh, and the rest were pressed or dried in the sun for raisins.

GROWING TIPS
A number of cultivated varieties will produce a good crop of ripe fruit in our climate. Plant the vine at the foot of a south-facing wall, after filling the hole where it is planted with good fertile earth, and the vine will flourish. With every leaf a new tendril is formed to give the young shoots support, which it will only find if there are other branches nearby. Thus, if the vine is grown against a wall, the young shoots must be regularly tied back to prevent them from being blown down.

You can start to pick the first bunches of grapes a few years after planting the vine. If the grapes are to grow larger, you have to cut out the smaller ones, removing half the fruit from every branch. If you do not do this, the individual grapes will be smaller. Prune the vine every year, keeping the main shoots which have developed, but cutting back the shorter, fruit-bearing branches to about 5cm every year in the autumn. This autumn pruning is extremely important.

You should never prune a vine in the spring when

the sap starts to rise. If the vine is pruned then, there is a danger that it will 'bleed to death'. Strong, fruit-bearing shoots are obtained by leaving one or at most two shoots on every branch that is pruned. The rest are removed at an early stage. These remaining shoots should also be tied up in good time, removing the supporting tendrils, because they do not serve any purpose and use up nutrients which should be used for forming fruit.

Ultimately the sun is essential for the development of the vine, the ripening process, and the final sugar content of the fruit. This is why the vine should also be pruned in summer, removing the leaves which cover the bunches of fruit, as well as those at the end of the fruit-bearing shoots. These can then be cut back to a point three leaves past the cluster of grapes. There is no danger of bleeding from pruning the vine in summer.

Grapes can easily be propagated by taking cuttings in winter.

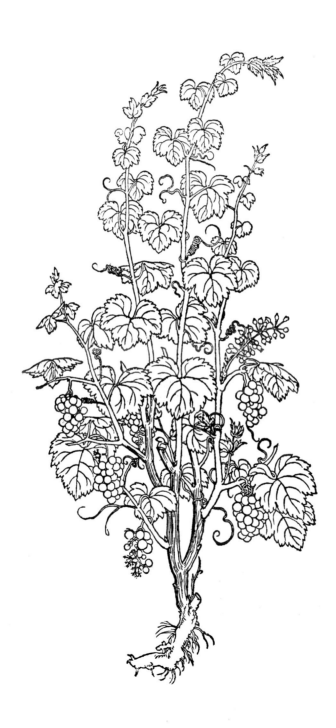

⟨✿⟩ BIBLE GARDENS TO VISIT

AMERICA

Cathedral Church of St. John the Divine, 1047 Amsterdam Avenue, New York, USA

Magnolia Plantation and Gardens, Route 4, Charleston, South Carolina 29407, USA

Missouri Botanical Garden, St Louis, Missouri, USA.

St. James' Lutheran Church, 110 Avenue Phoenetia, Coral Gables, Florida, USA.

AUSTRALASIA

Bible Garden, 12 Mitchell Road, Palm Beach, NSW, Australia.

Rockhampton Botanic Garden, Queensland, Australia.

Rutland Street Chapel, Christchurch, New Zealand.

ASIA

Neot Kedumim (Biblical Landscape Reserve in Israel), Kiryat Ono, Israel

EUROPE

Redcliffe Missionary Training College, 66 Grove Park Road, Chiswick, London W4, England.

Royal Botanic Gardens, Kew, Richmond, Surrey, England.

St. James's Church, Piccadilly, London, England.

Bangor Cathedral Close, Bangor, Caernarvon, Wales, UK.

Hortus Botanicus van de Vrije Universiteit, Van der Boechorststraat 81081 BT Amsterdam, Nederland